Picture of Defeat

PICTURE OF DEFEAT

John Harris

HUTCHINSON
LONDON MELBOURNE AUCKLAND JOHANNESBURG

© John Harris 1988

All rights reserved

First published in Great Britain in 1988 by
Century Hutchinson Ltd,
Brookmount House, 62–65 Chandos Place,
London WC2N 4NW

Century Hutchinson Australia Pty Ltd
PO Box 496, 16–22 Church Street, Hawthorn, Victoria 3122,
Australia

Century Hutchinson New Zealand Limited
PO Box 40-086, Glenfield, Auckland 10, New Zealand

Century Hutchinson South Africa Pty Ltd,
PO Box 337, Bergvlei, 2012 South Africa

Set by Avocet Marketing Services, Bicester, Oxon.
Printed and bound in Great Britain by
Anchor Brendon Ltd, Tiptree, Essex

British Library Cataloguing in Publication Data

Harris, John, *1916*
   Picture of defeat.
   I. Title
   823'.914 [F]   PR6058.A6886

ISBN 0-09-173451-0 *Invalid
– see jacket*

Author's Note

After its liberation by the Allies in 1943 following the landings at Salerno, Naples was in a very poor state of health. Called the only eastern city in the west and the place where Europe joined Africa, the city had been looted by the Germans, the British, the Americans, the French, the Poles and anyone else who happened to pass by. Italian art treasures disappeared to all corners of the globe and some have still not been found.

The situation was confounded by the fact that AMGOT, Allied Military Government of Occupied Territory, largely in the hands of the American army, was infiltrated by Italian crooks.

To confuse matters further, the surrounding countryside contained bands of partisans who included Communists, genuine patriots, escaped prisoners of war, and ex-soldiers of the Italian army who were simply trying to avoid being called up to fight for the Germans. Alongside them, but operating solely for gain, were gangs of bandits – some of them Allied deserters, some crooks who had been too hastily freed from gaol by the opponents of the Fascist régime – who had armed themselves with weapons picked up on the battlefields.

Unfortunately, also, too many AMGOT officers, chosen for their ability to speak Italian, turned out to be contacts – even relations – of the crooks. Though many attempts were made to break up the rackets, the AMGOT officers closed ranks and those who dug too deeply into the activities of the underworld found they lost promotion. With Naples starving and its people willing to sell both body and soul to obtain a meal for themselves or their families, it was a situation ripe for exploitation, which made it very difficult for anybody to be honest.

For details I am very much indebted to *Naples '44*, by Norman Lewis, and *Rome, '44* by Raleigh Trevelyan.

5

I

1

Naples smelled of burned-out houses and choked sewers. In every restaurant braziers used a form of incense to kill the smell that somehow managed to seep up through the floor.

There were ruins everywhere. Whole streets were blocked with landslides of masonry, bomb craters and twisted vehicles, and there was no water because the air raids in August had smashed the mains and they had never been properly repaired. Everyone was dependent on the water sellers who brought water round from a well somewhere near Santa Lucia, because, to finish off the damage done by Allied bombers, the departing Germans had sent round demolition squads to destroy anything that worked and might still be of value. With people forced to use dubious sea water for cooking, there was a great sale of distilling devices. Most of them didn't work and had been put together by crooks quick to seize on the city's misery to make money.

Field Security had taken over the Pizzoni Palace, one of the splendid buildings on the Riviera di Chiaia at the Santa Lucia end of the Via Caracciolo. It was a three-storey building looking out over the Castel dell' Ovo and the Porto Santa Lucia, and was decorated in ornate Neapolitan marble. Field Security occupied the main floor at the head of a splendid frescoed staircase.

Every room seemed to have wall-to-wall mirrors, the painted ceilings were hung with enormous chandeliers, and the gilded furniture made the place look like Versailles. But there was no hot water or heating and the lavatory was in what appeared to be a scullery on the

9

ground floor. There was nothing to indicate who Field Security were and most Neapolitans thought they were the British equivalent of the recently departed SS.

The view at the front of the Palace was the Bay of Naples, the sea, statues and palm trees – all contrived for the pleasure of the nobility who had once lived there. The rear windows, however, looked down on an ugly little group of narrow courts where most of the rooms had been taken over by people running a variety of small businesses – an old man who made ornaments, brooches and candlesticks from bone, a man whose job was printing pamphlets for the Communists, a tinker, a broom-maker, a tripe seller with her chalked notice, *Trippa Assortita*, a man who sold vegetables, a macaroni vendor, a basket maker. With their little handcarts parked in front of their premises, the screaming children, the women doing their washing or preparing meals, sometimes it looked like a crowd scene from a provincial opera.

But Naples itself, of course, was like a scene from an opera. Everybody knew everybody else, and the lowly who inhabited the rear of the palace had formed their own little villages and, because most of what they needed was obtainable on the spot, rarely left them. Naples was full of such rookeries, all teeming with people, many of them living as whole families in single windowless rooms and conducting most of their lives on the pavement outside, and the city was like an anthill, always occupied with the activities of petty crime.

Liberated the previous autumn by the Anglo-American landing at Salerno, Naples had risen against its German occupiers and fought them for three days with great loss of life. Now, struggling to get back on its feet but exhausted by the war, it was starving. People had been trudging miles outside the city to raid farms and dig up anything eatable they could find, impervious to the threats of the furious farmers, even trying to net sparrows and warblers drawn by the fruit in the

10

orchards. Now, after the winter, the land was bare and, near Zi' Teresa's at Santa Lucia, the rocks, which were normally covered with limpets, had been stripped bare by children using screwdrivers and old army knives. The winkles had been taken long since. Though the limpets by no means made a meal, if boiled in a broth of odds and ends of chicken intestines, they gave a faint flavour that was better than nothing. The Neapolitans could not afford to be choosy and, since crooks were running the black market, it didn't pay to enquire too deeply into what was going on.

But it was beginning to look as if Tom Pugh had, because somebody had tried to toss a hand-grenade into the back of the Jeep he was driving.

Tom Pugh had arrived in Italy on the first day of the Salerno landing. Some of the men ahead of him were still laid out under blankets awaiting burial, and shooting was still going on. Since Field Security saw fit to arm its members only with Webley pistols and five rounds of ammunition, he wondered what the hell he was there for.

He was in Field Security because he had spent three years in Italy before the war and spoke excellent Italian. After university he had qualified as a lawyer and got himself married on the strength of it. But, just as he was settling down in the firm of Bannister, Hacker and Lee, his wife had run off with the junior partner and, since he had some ability as a painter – at school he had walked off with every art prize available – he had bitterly decided to give up law and chance his arm as an artist. After three years of existing on a shoestring – easier in Italy because food was cheaper and it was warmer and the Italians liked artists – Hitler had ruined everything by starting the war. Since he was a long way from a recruiting office and Italy was not at first involved, he had stayed where he was; but then Mussolini had shown clear signs that he intended to join Hitler, and

Pugh had deposited the few canvasses he considered worth keeping with Signora Foa, the old lady with whom he lodged at Severino Campagna near Frascati, burned the ones he didn't and caught what turned out to be the last British ship out of Brindisi.

Safely back in England, he had immediately been called up and, like other men who were found to possess linguistic ability, had been directed into the Intelligence Corps. He had vaguely expected to spend his time interviewing German prisoners and extracting from them, by a variety of devious means, information that would eventually lead to the winning of the war.

It hadn't turned out like that.

Four months of basic training had been followed by two months at the Corps Depot at Winchester which taught him nothing except how to ride a motor cycle and how to turn round on a parade ground in good military fashion without falling over his own feet. Only in the final weeks of his course in the north of England had he received any instruction on how to behave as an Intelligence operator

He'd joined Field Security happily enough, however, because Captain Gwyn Griffiths Jones, who was now his commanding officer, had been at school with him and had assured him that, with his knowledge of law, art and the Italian language, he was just the man they wanted. Gwyn Jones had always looked after Pugh, keeping the bullies off him when he'd been small; when Pugh gave up law they'd lost touch until war had brought them together again.

It was only when he was well and truly part of it that Pugh had begun to wonder if Intelligence was the best job for him. Perhaps, he thought, he might have been better in a bigger unit where he didn't have to work so much alone. But he'd always worked alone, which was probably why he'd opted out of law for painting, but now he found he had no friends in England and sometimes there seemed to be almost too much emptiness about him.

He had arrived in North Africa soon after Alamein and the American landings in the west had carried the Allies to French-owned Morocco and Algeria. Since the fighting had appeared to be over there, his job was supposed to be to bridge the gap between the military and the civilian population but, since neither he nor the military knew exactly what that meant, liaison was usually less than satisfactory. His officer had been given the job because he not only spoke Spanish – which, as it had the same Latin base, was considered to be similar to French – but also had spent some years in West Africa and mastered the Temne and Mende tribal languages, with which it was assumed he could talk to Arabs.

Because North Africa was the first of the Allied victories, nobody knew what the duties of Field Security consisted of but it was laid down that its men were not to be used merely as interpreters, who were considered to be two-a-penny types of a much lesser breed. Nobody had any idea of the political situation they were facing or that the Arabs were even then considering ways and means of getting rid of their French overlords, and most of their activities were based on trial and error. Almost the first thing they did was to release from gaol a man who had convinced them he was an ardent patriot who had been imprisoned for his stand against the Germans. By the time they discovered he was a leader of an Algerian gang under sentence of death for murder it was too late and he had vanished.

It was as they were trying to work out how they might recapture him that Field Security was reorganised for the invasion of Italy. Pugh ended up attached to the American Fifth Army and four days later sailed for the landing at Salerno. A month later Jones heard of him and he found himself in Naples.

They were now well established. Only Captain Jones lived in the Pizzoni Palace. The sergeants had small apartments in the Casa Calafati, a large house nearby, which had been turned into a sort of residential hotel

13

without catering, and took their meals in an army canteen. Pugh occupied an apartment on the top landing. It had a parquet floor and, as you entered, the door of the wardrobe at the other side of the room automatically swung open and the loose parquet blocks leapt and danced all the way to the window. The light switch was a turntable type that had to be twisted completely about four times before contact could be made, and the lavatory was at least a kilometre way, at the end of a blocked-off passage long enough to bowl bumpers down, and not without hazards: the lock didn't work and the door was too far away to jam a foot against. Nevertheless, the Casa Calafati, though like an icebox during the winter, was comfortable enough by Neapolitan standards. Pugh had a bedroom and a small sitting room with a sofa, and a gas ring to make coffee.

To give the place a lived-in atmosphere, other residents had been allowed to remain. Two prostitutes occupied rooms on the floor below, so that customers tramped regularly up the stairs. But the prostitutes were cheerful souls who sometimes sent up plates of spaghetti to the soldiers in exchange for cigarettes. The other sergeants in the place were often away, occupied on some task in the outer spaces of their area, but Sergeant Patrick O'Mara – who displayed all the contrariness of the Southern Irish by electing to fight for the nation he insisted had oppressed his homeland – was usually around, often sharing his room with a small plump Italian girl he intended to marry when the regulations were slackened.

"'Twill work out,' he said. 'I'm Irish. She's Italian. And the Irish and the Italians have always been nearest to God's heart. You've only to look at the number of Celts an' Latins in the calendar of saints to see that.'

Another sergeant, Plummer, had a girl who merely turned up from time to time, while Sergeant Waddilove preferred to take advantage of the proximity of the prostitutes, because he always seemed to be too busy for

14

any other dalliance. Pugh, who suspected that Waddi-love had his finger in a few other pies, had so far lived a lonely celibate life, not entirely through choice but because he hadn't yet met someone whose chatter he could stand for long. He had always been a self-reliant man, but he had become even more of a loner after his marriage had broken up. Moreover, a loner with a quick temper which had not helped to win him a lot of friends.

The owner of the house, Maria Calafati, claimed to be a countess, but there were so many women in Italy claiming to be contessas it was hard to tell. She was tall and gaunt, with purple sacs under her eyes and greying hair pulled back from her face. Normally she wore black and always smoked too much – the cigarettes gifts or bought on the black market – and she was an insomniac, so they could always hear her at night as she lay on her bed smoking, reading and coughing.

The work was not arduous, but it became apparent at once that the man who had imagined that a few British and American Security agents could put Naples to rights must have been out of his mind. It had been a thieves' kitchen as long ago as the days when Tiberius had his villa at Capri, and Neapolitans had been learning new tricks ever since. The Field Security Sections – usually an officer and a dozen sergeants who were located in all the principal cities or ports where there were British troops – had taken their measure within a matter of days, though it hadn't done either side a lot of good. The Neapolitans continued exactly as before and the Field Security Section, having come to the con-clusion that never in a million years would they change the Neapolitans, had simply nibbled at the edges and hoped for the best.

They had captured a carload of Fascist police archives and documents from the German Consulate, including a black file containing a mass of denunciations of Italians by other Italians – most of them useless because they were the work of malicious or envious neighbours and

15

consisted of nothing but vague descriptions, as if a guilt complex had prevented the accusers from being too exact. No one was very certain of the future, anyway. The Neapolitans were just beginning to draw breath after the liberation and wonder how they were going to live, because the Allies, concerned with fighting the Germans, had never given enough attention to making sure Naples was fed. As one of the men Pugh arrested told him, they had been buggered about by the Germans and now they were being buggered about by the Allies. 'When the Germans were here,' he said, 'we ate occasionally. Now we eat *very* occasionally.'

To the hungry Neapolitans food had become all-important. The one thing in the mind of every one of them was how to produce enough food for themselves and their families. They would eat anything, and go to any lengths to obtain it, though they had never been unused to hunger because, in the south, Italians had often eaten little more than bread dipped in olive oil; but now, at the end of the winter, hunger had become starvation.

Anything was worth stealing – even from friends. Food, if it was there. If it wasn't, then anything that could be sold for money to buy food. One of the great jokes going about the city was that, unseen by sentries, thieves climbed the fortifications of Castellemare Castle and removed the wheels of Allied vehicles before escaping back over the towering walls with their loot. All that could be said in the way of consolation was that the Germans had suffered equally, and when they had opened an army boot repair shop, half the footwear deposited there had mysteriously disappeared into the Irish Consulate next door and out at the other side for the poor of the city.

But that was nothing. Lorries left for only an hour were found to be minus their wheels, because the Neapolitan gangs had developed a technique of removing wheels, spare parts, hoods, even engines, at an amazing speed. A tank had been stripped down day by day until nothing was left, and buses were driven to the hills, where they could be reduced at leisure to a skeletal framework; trams, left standing when the departing Germans had smashed the power supply, disappeared overnight. Railway engines vanished and fishing vessels were found miles inland. Even manhole covers had been found to have some value and the streets became full of lethal hazards. Nothing that wasn't screwed down was safe. Tombstones and marble statuary vanished from the cemeteries. The Americans were perfect dupes for the cunning Neapolitans, and many a marble angel taken from a graveyard had been reconstituted and sold as a Madonna sculpted by Orcagna, Bellini or one of the Pisanos. Even the heads from bomb-wrecked statues had been passed off as fragments of Michelangelo's work and sold for incredible sums of money.

The looting was not confined to the Italians either. Colonel da Sangalla, a Roman art expert in the uniform of the Italian army, had made it very plain that even British officers had sticky fingers. In fact, Pugh suspected that Da Sangalla himself, despite being attached to the Ministero di Monumenti e Belli Arti – the new government organisation for the protection of monuments and fine arts – had, like every other Italian, been forced beyond honesty by the prevailing circumstances and the need to stay alive, and had not been against helping himself.

It was difficult, in fact, to know where to look for an honest man. Hunger was a powerful goad, and the only truly honest policeman Pugh had ever come across among the lower ranks was an old hungry-looking bachelor. And with the miserably paid police inevitably open to bribes, the rackets taken over by experts, and not only Allied soldiers but officials of the Allied Military Government assisting, it was hard to see how Naples could ever be anything else but a hotbed of corruption. Even Vesuvius registered its protest by

17

erupting in March; a black motionless cloud of smoke hung over the city and made the air foggy with falling ash for days.

Yet there was still something about the place. Built round its beautiful bay, Naples demanded affection. Superstitiously religious, teeming, noisy and vital, it had a strange appealing warmth that always won Pugh's heart. He had done a lot of painting there and at Posillipo, Sorrento, on the slops of Vesuvius, or on Capri or Ischia, and he found it hard to condemn the southern Italians, abandoned as they always had been by Rome and the industrial north.

Most of his work consisted of winkling out Fascists and collaborators, screening line-crossers and Italians wishing to be employed by the Allies, investigating the people accused by informers of being German spies signalling to the enemy, and checking up on the eager virgins who were wanting to marry British soldiers. Most of the spies turned out to be harmless eccentrics, their signals the flashing of torches as they headed down the garden for the lavatory. Of the thirty-odd would-be brides he had checked, at least three-quarters were on the game. It was reckoned that thousands of desperate women, their men dead, disappeared or trapped in the north, were at it. Sometimes it made him heartsick at the tragedy.

Most of the people were unemployed, their faces pale with hunger, their bodies swollen, their eyes and faces puffy with starvation, or so thin their clothes hung from them like sacks. Those who could stayed in bed all day, and parents offered their daughters in return for a good meal for them. There were no cars – only carts and carriages drawn by skeletal horses. It was impossible to put anything down for a moment without having it stolen, and the *scugnizzi* – the urchins of Naples, both male and female – had developed a technique of scrambling over the tailgates of moving army lorries and off-loading anything they could to their friends

18

running behind. It brought a few lost fingers as hidden guards chopped with bayonets at the hands that appeared over the tailgate, and a few deaths as children slipped and fell under passing wheels.

As the weeks went by, things grew no better and the growing impudence of the black market operators took the breath away. The Americans were the power in the Allied Military Government and many of them, hand-picked for the invasion, were of Italian descent. Some of them were suspected of working hand in glove with the people who ran the black market, which was known to be headed by Vito Genovese, second-in-command of a New York Mafia family until he'd fled Italy before the war to dodge a murder charge. He had become a friend of Mussolini and, on Duce's downfall, had transferred his allegiance to AMGOT. Without any doubt, he was now the power behind the scenes, appointing his friends to important positions, leasing out rackets, demanding pay for favours done – and exacting punishment for anyone who crossed him. Liberation had become confused by corruption.

After six months of freedom, the black market operation was becoming organised, the stolen military stores – apart from guns and ammunition, which were sold under the counter – were being offered openly. But no matter how many small-timers were arrested, the big ones always escaped because the petty thieves they employed found it safer to go to prison for perjury than to incriminate their masters. Even the air raid sirens were said to go at pre-arranged times so that, under cover of the smoke screens put up to hide the city from the approaching raiders, the black marketeers could move in to do their work. Joints of meat disappeared from army stores, with coal, carpets intended for officers' quarters, instruments for hospital operating theatres – all slipped out of camp in army lorries driven by men, both civilian and military, in the pay of the gangs. Tailors all over Naples were turning looted uniforms into civilian clothes. Dyed bright colours, army long johns became fashionable garments. Even a car from the Papal Legate's office was found to have stolen tyres. Nothing was safe. People in cafés drank out of cut-down bottles because all the glasses had been stolen. The orchestra at the opera house, returning from a break between the acts of *Tosca*, found half their instruments stolen, and mediaeval costumes taken from the theatre had reappeared, re-fashioned as sportswear. A few raids were put on here and there, but there were always too many people wearing overcoats made from Canadian blankets who could claim the patronage of this or that senior officer for anything ever to come of them.

Because Field Security had pulled off a few small successes but never anything very big, they suspected there was a leak somewhere in their organisation. People they had their eye on had a habit of disappearing. Black market goods they knew existed vanished before they arrived. Somewhere in the organisation someone was passing on information. Jones had all the sergeants in his office, lectured them, questioned them, threatened them. It was Pugh's belief, however, that the leak wasn't among their own personnel but someone outside who knew what was going on. So they watched the civilian personnel they employed, the clerks, the typists and the cleaners, but they were able to pin nothing on any of them.

It was quite by chance that Pugh was the one who fell for investigating the penicillin racket. He'd been working with Sergeant O'Mara to pull in an Italian who had made 25,000 dollars from stolen tyres. They had put a surveillance on a garage in the Via Villari where they knew the stolen tyres were being kept, watching from the loft above the stable of an old man called Mori, who ran a threadbare carter's business. He had an ancient sway-backed grey horse called Urbino that reminded

20

Pugh of the pictures he'd seen in Devon pubs of the story of Widdicombe Fair with the ghost of Tom Pierce's grey mare 'all gashly white.' It pulled a ramshackle cart with which old Mori earned his living moving things about the city. At the moment, after the bombings and with the repeated air raids, he was making a better living than he ever had hauling rubble away for the Allies and dumping it beyond the city boundary.

Now, with the tyre deal behind them, Pugh found himself involved in something more important. By this time the theft of military stores had become so acute that items which could be bought freely on the black market were found to be in short supply for the army. While the army needed technical equipment, that which had been shipped out to them was being sold openly in the Via Roma, and while sick civilians could go to a pharmacist for a course of penicillin injections, supplies were becoming non-existent in army hospitals. The black market was beginning to affect the war effort, and it happened to fall to Pugh to investigate it.

In fact, it wasn't as difficult as he'd expected. Everybody knew about it and there was a surprising openness about acknowledging it existed. Feeling it was going to be easy and already seeing himself promoted and given a medal, Pugh called on a hospital dispenser he knew who had always been willing to talk. This time, though, he wasn't. In the end he offered the name of a man called Tirandolo who lived near the Vomero district, but he warned Pugh that nobody would be prepared to give evidence against him.

'Why not?' Pugh demanded sharply.

The dispenser shrugged, waggled his eyebrows and moved his hand backward and forward. 'He belongs,' he said.

'Belongs to what?'

'To the organisation.'

'What organisation?'

'I don't know its name, only that it will look after him.'

21

'The Mafia?'

The dispenser merely shrugged again.

Checking the name, Pugh found that Ugo Tirandolo was indeed known to deal in penicillin but, as he had been warned, he also learned that he was known to be under the protection not only of Vito Genovese but also of someone in AMGOT who contrived to remain unknown.

The next move was to contact an old drinking companion, Agent Walter Szogoscz, of American Counter-Intelligence. Szogoscz and Pugh had often worked together and celebrated their successes together, and CI were well in with AMGOT. They had a magnificent filing system but unfortunately none of them could speak Italian, so that they had to rely on British Field Security. Like all Americans, Szogoscz was generous and always willing to lend a Jeep in exchange for a bottle of whisky. He knew about Vito Genovese but preferred to steer clear of him because other American officers who had enquired too deeply had found themselves passed over for promotion. In the end, it was decided that Pugh should try.

Tirandolo had a splendid house like a small palace on the slopes to the north of the city. There was an Alfa Romeo outside and Pugh was shown in by a liveried footman. The place was full of paintings, magnificent drapings and old furniture. Tirandolo was an over-weight elderly man wearing a smart blue suit, a pink tie and an ingratiating smile. He offered Pugh a drink and merely shrugged when Pugh told him why he was there. He remained bland and unperturbed when Pugh started to search his house and showed no alarm whatsoever when he finally found an empty carton that had contained penicillin in the car. He was still magnificently unmoved when Pugh announced he was going to arrest him.

'I would recommend great care, Sergente,' he said, a glint in his eye that boded ill for Pugh. 'I happen to be related to an Allied officer of great power. I think you would do your work better in North Africa and I can easily see that you are removed.'

Feeling it was a sign he was winning, Pugh returned to headquarters, where Captain Jones listened to him with a certain amount of anxiety.

'Have you informed Colonel Tasker?' he asked.

'No.'

'Well, you'd better. You know he always insists on knowing what's going on.'

'I can never see the bloody point,' Pugh growled. 'He's not part of our organisation.'

'He's the boss, all the same. The superior officer. We're attached to his department for pay, rations, discipline, hiring and firing, and, for that matter, everything appertaining to life and death. That's the way it is in the army. Somebody has to be boss, and in our case it's Tasker. And, in case you hadn't noticed, that means that what he says goes. Besides' – Jones frowned – 'I don't like this involvement with stolen drugs. I think you're asking for trouble.'

'I want to know who's supplying the bastard. Somebody is, and he must be Army.'

'Leave it.'

'Too late,' Pugh said. 'It's already fixed.'

'I think you should give it to the Americans. It's their baby.'

'It was the Americans who suggested I have a go. Agent Szogoscz.'

Jones's eyebrows rose. 'Why? Is he scared to have a go himself?'

'It'll be all right.'

Jones sighed and pushed across a newspaper. 'Column four,' he said. 'Your buddy, Bocco Detto Banti.'

'Who?'

'Boccaccio Detto Banti.'

The name rang a bell. Boccaccio Detto Banti was an Anglo-Italian painter like Dante Gabriel Rossetti, and

23

lived at Vicinamontane to the north. He had lived in England for much of his life, but when his Fascist sympathies had begun to show before the war in indiscreet comments, his popularity had dropped and he had returned to Italy, claiming to be an Italian. Such was his fame, he had been accepted without question because he was able to add a few laurels to Mussolini's shabby crown.

'What's happened to him?' Pugh asked.

'He's on his last legs. Didn't you know him before the war? Drop on one knee at the foot of the master sort of thing?'

Pugh nodded. 'I once visited him,' he admitted. 'Thought I might learn something. I needed to learn something somewhere. Nobody wanted to buy my paintings and I was genteelly starving.'

'Did he help?'

Pugh shook his head. 'He was already too old. He just rambled.'

'Wonder what'll happen to his paintings.'

'There aren't any.' Pugh said. 'He suffered from arthritis, I heard, and all he had were sold to keep the wolf from the door. There hasn't been a new one for years.'

'Perhaps you ought to go and make sure.'

'I'll stick with Tirandolo.'

Jones sighed. He was a tall, elegant man of some wit and, unlike many elegant men, was of a kind and gentle disposition. He had often found Pugh, who was shorter and thick in the body – thick in the head too, Jones often thought – difficult because, like many people of a similar stature, he was inclined to be aggressive and too quick to act.

He ran a hand over his face. It was pale, because he was fair-haired and the Italian sun made him go fiery scarlet and peel until he looked like a snake shedding its skin. 'Well, try to look like a soldier,' he suggested.

'I look like a soldier,' Pugh said indignantly.

24

'With a red handkerchief round your neck instead of a collar and tie? You look like Augustus John in an off-moment.'

'I wish I did. I shouldn't have to shave. John wore a beard.'

'You make the British army look as if it's staffed by a lot of Montmartre daubers. Artists don't go about like that these days.'

'I did.'

'I'm talking about *good* artists.'

Two days later, wearing a collar and tie as instructed, Pugh saw Tirandolo in prison at Poggio Reale. He had the best cell in the place – more like a private room – and it was obvious it was being cleaned by someone else, and he was having his meals sent in from outside. A squarely built man with heavy black eyebrows and a wide mouth like the slit of a letterbox was just leaving.

'A friend,' Tirandolo explained. 'Come to bring his greetings.'

Pugh found himself wondering if he had also tried to slip Tirandolo a file.

Tirandolo was still unperturbed, and claimed to know no details about the racket in penicillin or the names of the people in AMGOT who were involved. He was quite certain he would be found not guilty when he was brought before the magistrates, and Pugh had a suspicion he was right because, although they had filled the prison with people who had been guilty of small crimes, so far not one of the big fish had been caught. Witnesses vanished or the prosecution was found to have bungled its cases, and the finest criminal lawyers in Italy, with whom acquittal was a certainty, could be obtained at a price.

It soon became clear that it was going to be impossible to find anyone who would give evidence against Tirandolo, and after a fortnight had elapsed the case was beginning to look hopeless. A week later it was announced that Tirandolo was suffering from a stone in his kidney and, as there were complications and the facilities in the prison hospital were not adequate, he would have to be removed to a civilian establishment. Pugh had no doubt that, if necessary, Tirandolo would submit to a shallow incision in his side to provide proof of an operation, but his recovery would be long and slow.

As he gave Pugh the news, the prison governor shrugged and waved his hand from side to side. Pugh knew what he meant. 'This is Naples and that's how things are done.'

For a long time Pugh brooded angrily on it, wondering if he ought to persevere. In the end he decided he should and he told Tirandolo that he intended to. Tirandolo smiled and said nothing, and it was the next day that the hand-grenade – doubtless, like everything else, acquired on the black market – was thrown at the Jeep. It hit the rear end, bounced off and burst in the road to kill a mule and an old man. Pugh was unharmed but it was enough to make him realise he was batting on a very sticky wicket.

'I think,' Jones said slowly, 'that it might be a good idea for you to go and check on those paintings of Bocco Detto Banti at Vicinamontane, after all.'

2

Pugh frowned. 'Isn't Vicinamontane right up near the fighting?'

Jones beamed. 'The German line runs through Venafro and Baranello to Vasto. It's not a lot further north.'

'There's an altarpiece there, isn't there? By Botticelli or somebody.'

'Not quite,' Jones said. 'It's by Simonetta and it's in the church of San Isidro at Avizano nearby.'

'It's supposed to be pretty good.'

'It's supposed to be priceless. I'm trying to get permission to have it brought to safety, if the Germans haven't nicked it. They hadn't, the last we heard.'

'They must be slipping. They've nicked everything else in Europe.'

'As long as Italy was an ally,' Jones pointed out, 'even an ally that was a liability, Hitler managed to hold off everybody who was wanting to grab anything valuable. But when Mussolini went and we landed, he issued an order – a *Führerbefehl* no less – that Italian art treasures were to be taken to the Reich to save them from the Anglo-American predators. As a result, art galleries began to evacuate their treasures and store them wherever they could for safety, in *depositos* – remote villas, farms, castles, monasteries. They thought – reasonably enough, I suppose – that we'd pinch 'em, and I suppose we did take a few. But in fact it was the Germans they ought to have worried about. They shifted everything they could carry from here to Cassino and then announced they were moving them to

27

the Vatican. It was looting carried out with good German efficiency, and it's my bet only a few arrived. You might look in on the old altarpiece while you're in Vicinamontane and see what the chances are of removing it.'

'What's the urgency? Are the Germans going to put in a counter-attack?'

'They aren't able to attack any more. They're finished.'

'They don't *seem* to be finished,' Pugh commented. 'They attacked like hell at Battipaglia.'

'That was in the early days.'

'They did again at Semo. They probably will at Vicinamontane.'

'You don't want to go, do you?'

'No.'

Jones sighed. 'Look, Tom, old lad,' he said, leaning his elbows on his desk, 'there are good reasons. You made the mistake of trying to smash the Neapolitan black market and it's obvious they want you removing. Tasker suggested you should handle it.'

'What have I done to Tasker?'

'You're too unaccommodating. I know there's a war on and people are a bit ruder in wartime than normally. They even shoot people occasionally. But you're well known for your temper, and, if it's of any interest to you, I've put you in for a commission. I bypassed Tasker with that one and I think you'll get it if you keep your nose clean.'

'I'm not so bloody sure I want a commission.'

'I didn't think you would,' Jones said wearily, 'but if I have my way you'll get no choice. It makes the journey easier and, with your knowledge of art and law, you're wasted as a sergeant. So keep out of trouble. Either you go back to North Africa or you go to Vicinamontane. The one thing that's clear is you've got to get out of Naples before someone puts a bomb under your bed.'

It seemed easier to go to Vicinamontane. At least it was a step nearer to Severino Campagna, where Pugh had stored his paintings in 1940 and there might be a chance of recovering them.

Nevertheless, he continued to protest. He didn't want to go to Vicinamontane and, stone or no kidney stone, he wanted to see Tirandolo nobbled. He knew he was involved with the penicillin racket and even if he'd been suffering from congenital leprosy he would still have enjoyed nobbling him. None of the rackets the war had let loose was worse than the traffic in drugs. Black marketeers did at least give you something in return for your money, even if what they offered was stolen and they grossly overcharged. Penicillin was different because they were dealing in death.

Medical orderlies had sold penicillin to civilian doctors for meningitis from the early days – and perhaps that was understandable, though it benefited only the rich – and nobody had worried too much when one of the orderlies was caught and punished. But lately the people behind the racket had begun to grow greedy and, as it had become more difficult for the orderlies to provide the stuff, the racketeers had started to dilute it with water or fine sand. The result was loss of limbs and lives, even madness. Pugh had been shown a few of the affected children by Agent Szogoscz, and it had become his dearest wish to put Tirandolo and the people behind him where they ought to be.

'Look,' he said, still trying to avoid Vicinamontane, 'I'm just getting dug in, in Naples.'

'Then,' Jones said, 'you'd better produce your little spade and dig yourself out again. People are after your blood. Why the hell did you let the Yanks get you involved in investigating this penicillin thing?'

'It was time somebody did,' Pugh said hotly. 'And I found traces of penicillin in his car.'

'So you stuck him in a cell at Poggio Reale. The big boys who're behind him promptly set to work to get him out.'

'With a doctor's certificate obtained by bribery.'

Jones sighed again. 'You can't beat them, Tom, old son. It'll drag on and on until he's finally allowed to go.'

'All the more reason why I shouldn't go to Vicina-montane. I didn't like the smooth bastard and I'm willing to risk a bomb under the bed to get him.'

'I'm not,' Jones said.

'Naples needs me.'

'So do a lot of other places. You're supposed to be able to cover everything. Especially art.'

Pugh reviewed his military history without much enthusiasm.

'What's so special about Bocco Detto Banti, anyway?'

'Well, for one thing, he's a long way from Naples and the people who threw that grenade at you. And also he's now dead.'

'When?'

'Yesterday. Rome Radio broadcast it. We picked it up. He was considered to be part of the rebirth of Italian art under Fascism. Didn't someone once call him the last of the Impressionists?'

'Well,' Pugh admitted, he was good at brushwork. But he hadn't much vision. He'd have been a great success as a magazine illustrator. The Italians' attitude to art these days is painstaking but a bit unoriginal. I always reck-oned he was a bit of a hack.'

'Not everybody did and' – Jones smiled – ' you're hardly competent to judge. You were a bit of a hack yourself.'

Pugh acknowledged the fact without bitterness, accepting that Jones, who was an old friend, wasn't being sarcastic or unpleasant, just realistic. 'You won't find him in the Louvre,' he argued.

'There are a lot of great artists who haven't ended up in the Louvre,' Jones said. 'The Impressionists were never very popular with galleries like the Louvre. But they're accepted now. Even Picasso used to be regarded a bit askance, but not any more. How do we know Detto Banti won't be the same?'

Pugh gave up his line of argument – he could see he was on a losing streak – and tried another. 'I'd have thought Naples was more important than a second division painter.'

'Of course Naples is important. But this is important too. It's been decided that somebody should look into it.'

'Who decided?'

'The High Altar. The word came down at once via Tasker. He said signals have been going back and forth between here and London like yo-yos.' Jones sighed. He got on well with his sergeants for the simple reason that most of them were better linguists than he was, but Pugh was always different. 'Now Detto Banti's dead the powers that be want to make sure the Germans don't get his paintings.'

'I bet there aren't any paintings. I only saw one or two when I was there.'

'There must have been a few he didn't tell you about. After all, you were hardly important enough for him to lay them out on the floor for you and ask you your opinion.'

It was Pugh's turn to sigh. 'He wasn't even Italian,' he said. 'He was English. Lived in Chelsea for years.'

'That's precisely why the powers that be have decided they want his pictures brought to safety. According to Tasker, they think that if we don't get them, they'll be dispersed and lost for ever. You know what the Italians are like. They'd sell their own grandmother.'

'I'm surprised the poor starving sods haven't tried eating her. How do we know the paintings haven't *already* been dispersed?'

Jones shifted restlessly. Sometimes he found Pugh hard work. 'The word's gone round the art dealers like a forest fire. Da Sangalla, of Monumenti e Belli Arti, is girding up his loins to see what he can do and if *he* gets his hands on them it's going to be difficult to get 'em off again. Even he might be too late. And Tasker says it was decided in London that Detto Banti was British and that

31

his paintings are part of the British art heritage.'

'Who decided?'

'Someone at a very high level.'

'There *can't* be any paintings,' Pugh said again. 'He couldn't hold a brush. I visited him.'

'That,' Jones said, 'is precisely why you've been chosen to visit him again. See his brother. He'll help. At least he will if he's got any sense, because he lived in England, too, and he's now busily claiming to be British.'

'So would I, if I lived here.' Pugh grinned. 'That's why half the girls in Italy are trying to marry British swaddies. How many paintings are there supposed to be?'

'Tasker says it's thought there are around a dozen. They were found in the cellar.'

'What were they doing there?'

'Does it matter, for God's sake?' Jones finally lost his temper. 'So long as they're *still* there. Did you meet the brother?'

'No. But I heard of him. Name of Marcopolo. Bocco paid for his keep and he did the small jobs about the place. Mixing colour. Making frames. Stretching canvas. Fetching the beer. That sort of thing. Anyway, why can't we just order a guard slapped on them? Can't we make an order forbidding their removal?'

'It wouldn't be much good if the Germans do put in a counter-attack in that sector. They could grab everything.'

Pugh's indignation showed. 'If I'm there they could grab *me*, too,' he said. 'And would the Germans want them? Detto Banti had nothing to do with Germany.'

Jones sighed. 'You've heard of Goering, I suppose?'

'He's that fat chap, isn't he?'

'Don't try to be funny! He's been collecting art treasures from all over Europe. It's known that that place he built near Berlin's full of stolen gems.'

'He won't want Detto Bantis,' Pugh insisted. 'If you'd said Rembrandt I might have understood it. Mind you,

Hitler might covet them. That tasteless bastard would grab *The Stag at Bay* if it had been painted by a German or an Italian. What about Detto Banti's family? Don't they have a claim to the bloody pictures? He married twice.'

'Both his wives predeceased him. He had no children.'

'Then won't his brother inherit them? Italian law's much the same as British law and they'll go to the nearest relative.'

'Look,' Jones' temper was growing hotter. 'I'm not interested in the ins and outs of it. Tasker says it's been decided that Detto Banti's English and that the paintings are wanted in England. Personally, I don't give a bugger about the bloody things. Walt Disney's about my limit as far as painting's concerned. See Tasker. He's the one who suggested it. He'll tell you more.'

Colonel Tasker had an office near the catacombs of San Placido and a suite of rooms in a hotel behind the church, with a batman to look after him so he could live in style.

His sergeant was in a bad temper. 'He's not here,' he snarled to Pugh. 'He's in the bloody O Sole Mio bar again.

Pugh smiled. It was common knowledge that Colonel Tasker spent a great deal of his time in the nearby bar, a smart little place with a small restaurant alongside where Tasker ate his meals, all done up – probably with American money – to attract American officers.

'If he could' – the sergeant sounded bitter – 'he'd conduct the whole bloody business of the British army in the O Sole Mio. The bugger's never here when we want him. He thinks being an officer consists of sitting back and drinking while the lads do the work. Whenever the general wants him or something like that, we have to send a runner down to dig him out.'

'What's the interest in the O Sole Mio?' Pugh asked. 'A barmaid?' He made shapes with his hands.

The sergeant scowled. 'Christ knows. There is one

but she's forty. Still' – his expression changed – 'he's fifty, so why not? But I wouldn't have thought she was his type. He prefers American Waves. Gets introduced to 'em by Baracca, that Yank colonel he knows. He likes the O Sole Mio, too. If it's important, you could nip down there. His car'll be outside. You can recognise the place by the horse tied to the lamp-post. Undertaker – name of Cirri – keeps his hearse round the back. As far as I can see, he spends more time shoving back the booze than he does shoving stiffs underground in the Campo Sterano cemetery. He probably supplies Tasker with bootleg brandy.'

'I think I'll wait,' Pugh said. 'He might not appreciate my interrupting a tête-à-tête with an undertaker.'

Tasker, a tall, plump, red-faced man who was running the military district, appeared half an hour later but made no apologies for his absence. He had once been in a good regiment but had left it before the war to go into one of the London financial houses, and returned in 1939. He was hand-in-glove with the Americans who were the power in AMGOT, and Pugh had often wondered if, like some of the Americans, he was hand-in-glove with Vito Genovese, too. Paintings had been cut from the frames in one of the occupied palazzos and a fifty-piece dinner set in Doccia porcelain had disappeared; and when some of the spoils were found carefully packed for taking home by air, Pugh had remembered that Tasker had a brother in RAF Transport Command. Colonel da Sangalla had certainly considered he'd been behind it.

Pugh tried to make his feelings clear. 'If we grab these paintings,' he said, 'we'll have the Italians coming down on our necks as the Greeks did about the Elgin marbles.'

Colonel Tasker glanced at the American officer sitting near his desk. Colonel Baracca was a handsome man of Italian extraction, with rimless glasses and a pencil-line moustache. It was said he had once tried to break into Hollywood but, discovering that though he

34

had the right features he hadn't the right ability, had settled to become an actors' agent. He and Tasker were great friends and Pugh had often wondered – assuming that Tasker was involved in one of the rackets – if Baracca was, too.

Tasker's mouth had tightened. 'The Italians are in no position to complain about anything,' he said.

Baracca nodded. 'Until September,' he observed, 'the bastards were in with the Krauts and they're existing now only because of our charity.'

'They're not doing much existing in Naples,' Pugh said bluntly. 'Most of them are starving.'

'Then, hell, it's up to them to put their house in order.'

'That's something they'll never do if everybody goes around helping themselves to their property. Who's the authority behind the request?'

'Commission for the Protection of Arts and Monuments,' Tasker said at once.

'And the Fine Arts and Archives Section of SHAEF,' Baracca added.

'Why are *they* interested? Bocco Detto Banti wasn't an American.'

'For God's sake, Pugh,' Tasker snapped. 'You've been given a job! Do it! You're the obvious man for it. You speak Italian. You know about art and you know about Italian painters because you've painted here. I'm told you even once met this bloody Detto Banti.'

'That won't help much now. He's dead.'

'His family will listen to you. And you know the law. I'm told you were once a lawyer, too.'

Baracca, who looked like a man who enjoyed money, stared at Pugh as if he were mad. 'Why'd you give up a career like that?'

'People do. Gauguin did.'

'Well, if you know the law,' Tasker said, 'you'll know how to get round it. You're to bring them back with you.'

'On the back of the motor bike?'

'You can acquire a car.'

'From the pool?'

'You'll provide it yourself.'

'Where from?'

'Dammit, Sergeant, commandeer one, if necessary! We're running this country. It gives us certain privileges. You'll be given funds. All we ask is that you bring those pictures back – no matter how many there are or how you do it. We want those canvasses. See we get them. And, Sergeant—'

Pugh halted in the doorway.

'Try, for the love of God, to look like a soldier instead of a fairground tout.'

3

Pugh's preparations for his departure north coincided with an air raid. Established now in what they called the Gustav Line, a line of fortifications which stretched right across Italy to the Adriatic, and determined to make the Allies fight every inch of the way north, the Germans were hitting back with counter-attacks and salients, and air raids on any city the Allies held.

As Pugh started to clear the paper from his desk, Sergeant O'Mara, a slight black-jowled man who enjoyed his clandestine domesticity in the Casa Cailafati with his Italian girl friend, appeared alongside him. He was investigating the theft by a British officer of a priceless collection of Roman jewels he was supposed to have been guarding. They had been replaced with imitations, and O'Mara found it funny.

'Sure to God, was he disgusted!' O'Mara always liked to behave in the way he thought stage Irishmen behaved. 'When he sold 'em, he found the originals had been changed before he arrived, and that what he'd pinched were imitations, too. The Eyeties are handlin' it now an' I'm doin' the report. It's goin' to take all day, too, so this one's for you.' He tossed a file down in front of Pugh. 'Peter Weedon, Private, Royal West Kents, otherwise Private First-Class Peter C. Weeden, US Army. He decided he'd be better paid as a Yank so he left our lot and joined theirs. 'Tis nabbed by the military police he's been as a deserter.'

Pugh studied the file. There was a sheet outlining the record of Pfc Peter C. Wieden of the 141st Regiment of the American Army, but there didn't appear to be much on it, save that, classed as absent without leave, he had been picked up in Naples by the American service police during an argument with a girl. Attached to it with a clip was a note. *'This man admits to being Private Peter Weeden, of the 6th Battalion, Royal West Kent Regiment. He's British. Passed to you for action. Arnold H. Baracca, Colonel.'* Appended to Baracca's note was another in the green ink Colonel Tasker liked to use. *'Our problem. Please attend to it.'*

O'Mara patted the file. 'You're a darlin' man,' he wheedled. 'There's no hurry, o'course.'

'In that case' – Pugh tossed the file into the pending tray – 'it won't do Private Weeden any harm to wait a little while. I've got a job at Vicinamontane.'

O'Mara's eyes widened. 'Is that a fact now? 'Tis dangerous up there.' Unlike the traditional Irishman and despite his presence in the British army, O'Mara didn't like the thought of trouble.

'Sure, Paddy,' Pugh agreed, 'but if the theft of thousands of pounds worth of penicillin can wait, so can Private Weeden, Colonel Tasker and Colonel Baracca.'

In a mutinous mood, he had just pushed back his chair when he heard the howl of the sirens and became aware of the smell of smoke from the mobile smoke-screen units that covered Naples against German bombers.

'Be the howly whirligig,' O'Mara yelled, vanishing like a rat up a drain, ''tis an air raid!'

Deciding he still had some time before heading for the shelter, Pugh found to his surprise that he hadn't and ended up standing with his back to the outside wall of the building while the windows blew in to set the black-out screens flapping like huge wings, and the whole district heaved and shuddered as if caught by an earthquake. Nobody in the immediate vicinity was hurt, but the house next door collapsed across the street in a torrent of bricks, mortar and old plaster. Because of it, he was unable to get away on time, and instead found himself calming terrified Neapolitans who thought it was another of the delayed-action devices left behind by the retreating Germans. These had resulted in more than one senseless massacre of civilians, and the city was reduced to a state of nerves every time a bang was heard.

As the smoke drifted away and the crowds dispersed, Pugh collected his motor cycle and rode to the Casa Calafati. It still had the chill of winter on it and the Contessa appeared, looking like Dracula's daughter, to offer him a glass of wine to speed him on his way.

'*Attenti*,' she said. '*Guardetavi dai tedeschi*. Look out for the Germans. They robbed me of everything I possessed.'

As he left, the old man who lived behind the Pizzoni Palace and carved things from bone appeared with a basket containing the statuettes, candlesticks and ornaments he'd made.

'Where do you get the bones?' Pugh asked.

'The San Placido catacombs, Signore.'

'See any Germans?'

The old man smiled. It was an old joke. Since strange noises at night were constantly reported by householders in the vicinity of the catacombs, it had been believed for a time that a group of Germans, cut off in the retreat, were hiding there, and then that it was a hideaway for deserters. A half-hearted search had been made but nothing was found and the monks, the guardians of the catacombs, chiefly a brother called Gregorio, insisted loudly that the catacombs were a holy place and the army shouldn't be there.

'The bones don't do much good there,' the old man said, 'and I don't take many. To listen to Brother Gregorio, you'd think they were his personal property instead of just the remains of a lot of dead Neapolitans.' He shrugged. 'Somebody might buy what I've made, and good Catholics, though they might have their eyes on the hereafter, still also have to eat.'

Pugh was glad to get away. But first he had to visit the Via Villari to see old Mori, the carter who had allowed them to use his premises to watch the tyre swindlers in the garage opposite. It was his job to deliver an envelope containing two large-denomination notes as a reward. It had to be done carefully, because there could be no indication of the old boy's cooperation, in case relatives of the arrested man wrecked his premises and slit his throat. He had therefore arranged to meet him in a bar, where he was able to slip the reward across without being seen.

The old man's jaw dropped when he realised what the envelope contained. *'Madonna mia,'* he said. 'I am a wealthy man! If ever I can help again, let me know. If you need anything moving! If you wish to store things! I have a loft. It has a few mice, of course, but not many.'

Pugh finally drove north in a downpour; as he climbed into the hills, it became a snowstorm. He was in a sullen frame of mind, certain by this time that Tasker was after the Detto Bantis for himself. All the best loot in Naples had already been picked over and here was a chance of acquiring something that could easily be transported – certainly more easily than grand pianos or marble effigies, for instance. He wondered if he could somehow manage to fail in his quest.

It hadn't been hard to acquire a car. He had approached Baron Viglionni, who lived in a vast decaying palace in San Pietro Pinnacolo near Caserta and could be relied on to fix anything that needed fixing. He had made fixing things his way of life, and the fact that he accepted money wasn't a matter of great concern because everybody did it, even the police. With inflation as it was, they were so shockingly short of money it was a wonder they managed to keep the law alive at all. For the most part, they didn't try very hard and merely concentrated on keeping the small fry from over-running the place. When Pugh had first arrived he had even been given a list setting out exactly what each individual expected as a hand-out for services rendered, from a mere carabiniere to an inspector who preferred

40

to keep his dignity by accepting not cash but a bottle of strega, a mozzarella cheese, even a packet of Keating's insect powder – because diseases were rampant and typhus, which hadn't arrived but was expected to, was carried by lice.

Viglionni, who preferred plain cash, knew where there was an old Fiat – much cannibalised for spare parts, he admitted – propped up in a garage without tyres and with some of its innards missing. Within twenty-four hours of Pugh turning up at his crumbling palace, which was empty of furniture but echoing with the cries of the people to whom he rented the multitudinous rooms, the spare parts appeared – doubtless stolen from another Fiat – and the tyres were on the wheels.

As Pugh climbed into the driving seat, Viglionni laid a finger alongside his aristocratic nose. '*Attenti*, Signor Sergente,' he said. 'Remember where you're going.'

Pugh nodded. 'I know,' he said. 'The Zona di Camorra – bandit country.'

The area north and east of Naples was a sort of no man's land where the peasants had once worked in conditions of near-slavery for the ancient families who owned the great estates. Nowadays, if anyone ruled it was the organised gangs, the Camorra. What had started as a secret society, evolved over generations to protect them against sweat shops and tax-collectors, had developed beyond the law and now knew only one set of rules: its own. The police were tolerated simply because, by keeping down the small-time crooks, they made life easier for the big ones. The gangs preyed on travellers, the army and the black market alike, and the present undisputed king of the area was a man by the name of Corneliano Romandi. Because he was said to be young, good-looking, affected gallant manners to women, was brave and above all took from the rich and gave to the poor – something which Pugh doubted very much – Romandi had created a sort of hero-worship for

41

himself among the Italians, who, after the corruption of Mussolini's régime, were desperate for someone to admire.

The road north was noisy with the roar of military traffic, both British and American. Every vehicle in the world seemed to be rumbling up and down it and every soldier in the world seemed to be riding in them – those going up, if not eager, at least clean; those coming down filthy, their eyes empty, their faces blurred by a fuzz of beard. If they hadn't been up before, the ones going up were singing. Those coming down always rode in silence.

The army's advance up Italy had been likened to that of a frustrated bull, weary but willing, butting its way head-down into assault after assault, street by street, house by house, so that men coming down weren't interested in where they were going, just that they were going there, and that ahead of them, away from the cold and the wet and the mud, there was a hot bath, clean clothes, sleep, and women – not necessarily for sex, but just to talk to, joke with, even merely to look at.

Caserta was its usual shabby self, muddy streets full of beggars surrounding the magnificent palace built by the Bourbons. In Posta, the centre of the town seemed to be full of British, Canadian and French service policemen, together with carabinieri armed with their ancient Carcano rifles. The military police looked worried and as Pugh waited to move through the traffic, one of them explained.

'The bloody Frog colonial troops went berserk at Cavaltino,' he said. 'There's a wholesale assault every time the bastards pass through anywhere.'

The French troops, known to the Allies, as *goumiers*, were hawk-faced Moroccans whose speciality was mountain fighting. They wore the Arab burnous and, though they carried rifles, like the Gurkhas they were also expert with their knives. They were not organised into normal military formations but into groups called

42

goums officered by Frenchmen, and had an uncanny gift for moving silently through the mountains and hills, their methods similar to that of an incoming tide on a series of sand castles. They disposed of opposition and pushed on regardless of what was happening to their right or left, and they had a habit of bringing back evidence of their victims in the shape of ears, noses, even heads. Unfortunately they were feared not only by the Germans but also by their own side. Known to the Italians as *marocchini*, they were noted for their indifference to death and their lust for women. Coming from the hills of French North Africa, they seemed totally unresponsive to discipline and had been a menace ever since they landed in Italy. Whenever they were in the vicinity, women locked their doors and went out only if accompanied by a man.

'There've been thirty-nine women raped,' the policeman said. 'It's bloody disgusting the way the sods behave! Some of the women have had to be taken to hospital and the rest are in bed. The sindaco's saying that if we don't sort the buggers out they'll sort them out themselves. And you know what that means: probably more people killed. So watch out for yourself.'

As he left, Pugh kept to the main roads for safety, but they were all noisy with military traffic. There was no difference between the British trucks and the American trucks except that the Americans drove faster. The British kept the regulation distance and moved at a sedate pace. The American vehicles, driven largely by black men, usually with a cigar as long as a torpedo stuck in their teeth, went flat out all the time. It seemed to work just as well.

As Pugh had expected, Vicinamontane gave the appearance of having only recently passed through the front line. In fact, it wasn't long since the Germans had been pushed out, and there were plenty of rumours that they were expected back at any moment. Jagged walls and deserted buildings loomed. Houses had been wrecked, their beams, doors, and window frames carried away to make fires, and the ground churned to a morass by tanks and lorries. To the north the fields were all pocked by shell craters. A few broken buildings carried a Red Cross flag or the insignia of a headquarters, with here and there a scrawled slogan written by some Italian indignant at seeing his country taken over by strangers – *Italia per gli Italiani!'*

Even before the war, the buildings in Italy had been either not quite finished or not quite falling down, and the war had only made it more so. In the square there was a statue of Garibaldi, but signallers had used it as a post from which to hang their telephone lines and wires were looped round the Liberator's head. The hand that had once held the sword of freedom now held nothing more aggressive than a notice: 'Ahead of here are minefields. Move carefully.' On the plinth someone had chalked 'Dust brings shells. Drive slowly.'

On the whole, though, Vicinamontane had not come off too badly. There had been no street fighting and the roads were not choked with rubble. Most of the damage was on the south side of the town and had been done by the Allied guns moving north. Now that the Germans had left, their gunners were having difficulty dropping their shells into the town because of the intervening hills.

It didn't take long to discover the Ca 'di Leone, the Detto Banti house. It was in the main square opposite the shabby Palazzo Municipale. It was a square, ugly place, almost as big as the town hall and, like most buildings in the war zone, had lost part of its roof and one or two windows and tiles, but there was a garden and an orchard and there were trees outside the door, so that the place still retained a sort of dilapidated dignity.

The people of Vicinamontane, who had fled to the hills as the Allies moved north and the fighting swayed around the town, had returned now, and at least the place looked alive. The damage was nothing like as bad as in some towns, and there were even a few girls – in dresses made from old curtains and coats made from stolen army blankets, but girls nevertheless – talking to the American soldiers waiting in the square by their trucks.

Pugh drove up to the front door of the Ca' di Leone, which was situated under a portico held up by pillars that had been pockmarked by bullets. The house seemed to be silent, even empty, so he pushed his way in cautiously. In the distance, just over the next line of hills, he could hear the rumble of guns and decided it might be a good idea to finish the job and get out again as fast as possible, before that counter-attack everybody expected finally arrived. Suddenly, Naples seemed amazingly cosy by comparison.

The hall was empty. There were no curtains at the windows, no carpet on the floor, no furniture – just a broken chandelier with most of its glass drops missing. The faded wallpaper was marked with squares where pictures had once hung.

He was still staring about him when a face appeared at the top of the stairs. It belonged to a small, plump woman dressed in black. Her hair was iron grey and dragged back so tightly it seemed to put a strain on her ears. Her eyes were like raisins and she had a solid growth of moustache on her upper lip.

'*Qui vedo?*'

Pugh explained who he was and why he was there, and the old woman came down to meet him. As she did so, two men appeared from a room on the right. One was a short, square man with heavy eyebrows and restless black eyes, who wore what looked like an evening dress jacket over a British army pullover, an American army shirt and a pair of mountaineer's green knickerbockers. There was mud on his shoes and a smear of white paint on his sleeve. The other was a thickset youth with a startlingly red face and fierce black eyes. He was carrying a long gun.

Without seeing Pugh, the red-faced youngster turned abruptly and disappeared towards the back of the house. As the other man approached, the woman shuffled off in the direction of what Pugh assumed was the kitchen.

'I'm looking for Marcopolo Detto Banti,' Pugh said.

The Italian nodded. 'I am Marco Detto Banti.'

'So you speak English?'

'I lived many years in Chelsea.'

'Which do you prefer? English or Italian? I can offer both.'

Detto Banti stared back at him shrewdly. 'It doesn't matter much, does it?'

Pugh acknowledged the fact and gestured in the direction in which the red-faced youngster had disappeared.

'Who's that?' he asked.

'Vittorio della Croce. He's the butcher's assistant. At least, that's what he is at the moment. He's actually a student, but the universities aren't functioning just now so he got a job working at the butcher's. But there's no meat either, so he doesn't know what to do with himself.'

'Why does he have a gun?'

'He wants to shoot Germans. He's a Communist. Most of the students are Communists these days. It's a reaction after Mussolini.' Detto Banti shrugged. 'It's no good, anyway, so I let him have it. It's ancient. You have to fill it with powder and make your own shot out of lead.'

'Italian civilians are forbidden to carry arms.'

Detto Banti shrugged again. 'He's trying to join the partisans. He thinks he's a hero, and the hills are alive with partisans. When the armistice was declared, the Germans issued an order that all Italian soldiers had to report in uniform to the nearest German headquarters. None of them did, of course. They disappeared into the hills. Della Croce's trying to raise arms so they'll accept him.'

'With a smooth-bore muzzle-loader?'

'You should see some of the weapons they've got.'

'Will they be of any use?'

'I shouldn't think so.'

'I'm interested in your brother's paintings.'

Detto Banti pulled a face. 'Everybody's interested in my brother's possessions. His car's gone. It wasn't much, but it vanished the day he died. Books have disappeared from his library. Some of the silver's gone.' He gestured in the direction where the old woman had vanished. 'I think Enrichetta's got that. What about the pictures? Are you hoping to buy them?'

'*I'm* not. But I think I've got a buyer for them.' I hope, Pugh thought, and so long as Tasker isn't expecting simply to help himself.

Detto Banti looked interested. 'Who?'

'I gather the British Government's interested. To be exact, the Commission for the Protection of Arts and Monuments.'

Detto Banti's eyebrows shot up. '*Mamma mia.*' He grinned. 'They'd pay well, wouldn't they? Governments are never short of money. Only the Italian Government. You'd better come upstairs to the studio. We're just looking at them now.'

The studio at the top of the stairs had a vast window facing north, and had obviously once been a bedroom. It had odd fragments of furniture in it, a large wooden manikin, drapes of cloth and a table so smeared with paint it was impossible to see the wood beneath. The whole floor was spotted with paint, too. Propped against the walls were the paintings, and in the centre was a large upright easel holding a single canvas about a metre square. It was being studied by an elderly man whose clothes hung from his fragile frame like curtains.

Detto Banti gestured at him. 'This is Avvocato Tassinari,' he said. 'He's the lawyer handling my brother's estate. He's here to see fair play.' He shrugged. 'Though I don't know why he's worrying. Bocco had no family and, as I'm his brother, the paintings are legally mine.'

4

It didn't take long to get down to business, and by evening Pugh was fully occupied.

Avvocato Tassinari, it appeared, came from Naples and was one of the hundreds of lawyers who lived in the city, most of them without ever practising. Though their parents had gone hungry to give them an education which would bring them a title – avvocato, ingeniere, dottore, professore – most of the time the titles were valueless because there wasn't any work to go with them, and their owners largely lived in poverty. Avvocato Tassinari, it seemed, was one of the luckier ones and eked out a fragile existence on a legacy that had always been a pittance and was now even more so with inflation, but was occasionally boosted by the small fees that he picked up from such as Boccaccio Detto Banti.

He was skinny, beak-nosed and grey-faced, but carefully dressed. His white shirt had a darned but well-starched collar and, though his suit was pressed, its frayed cuffs betrayed its age. Despite his fragile appearance – he looked as if the slightest breath of wind would carry him away – his mind was alert and shrewd, and he was obviously not prepared to take the newly discovered Detto Bantis either at face value or on Marco Detto Banti's word.

By this time, a column moving north had halted in the square outside to disgorge men who were clearly due to move to the front. Under the trees in front of the church, lorries were parked and khaki-clad figures, laden down with equipment, were beginning to line up. The windows round the square were crowded with watching people. Officers conferred with local officials. A man walked his dog between the vehicles, and the dog lifted its leg against a wheel. Girls had appeared in doorways, smiling and waving, watched by the soldiers with eyes full of lust.

Pugh turned from the window. The Ca' di Leone was only half-full of furniture. 'We had to sell it,' Marco explained, pouring wine from a bottle. 'Or burn it for firewood. Bocco was running out of cash. He always overspent and he hadn't sold anything for years. A lot of it went soon after the war started.'

'When did he die?'

'Two days ago. He knew he was going. He had himself dressed and carried to the top of the stairs to say goodbye to his friends. There were only two of them. The rest had died or left the district. He had a great sense of the dramatic.'

'And the funeral?'

'Tomorrow. If the *tedeschi* don't come.'

'Are they going to come?'

'You bet they are.'

'Are you a Fascist?'

'I hated the bastards. Another drink?'

Pugh held out his glass, his eyes on the painting on the easel.

'From his vineyard,' Marco said, holding up the bottle. 'I looked after it, of course, not Bocco. At least, it won't send you to sleep with your head in the soup. There'll *be* soup. Enrichetta always provides something, even if it's uneatable.'

'Paid for how?'

'We sell something. This place was full of junk, and the Americans love junk. Great ones for souvenirs. We had a dead German in the garden when they left. I sold the buttons off his tunic at a dollar a time.'

Pugh was staring at the picture, his nose pressed close to the canvas.

'Is this really a Detto Banti?' he said.

Marco appeared from behind the easel. 'Of course it is!'

'Are you sure?' Avvocato Tassinari demanded.

'What else would it be?'

'How did it turn up?'

'There are always unwanted paintings round an artist's studio.'

'These weren't *around*.' Tassinari said firmly. 'They were in the cellar.'

Pugh frowned. 'And if there were pictures,' he asked, 'why didn't he sell *them* instead of the furniture?'

'These were hidden. Otherwise, there were only *sketches*.'

'Which you've sold?'

Marco grinned. 'Bocco let me have the pick of anything he didn't want.'

Avvocato Tassinari interrupted. 'This is the estate of Boccaccio Detto Banti,' he pointed out sharply. 'I was his lawyer and I am his executor. There had better not be anything more which you had the pick of. As it is, I'm troubled by the absence of sketches to go with *these* paintings. He must have made preliminary drawings.'

'Who wants pencil sketches?'

'I do.' There was a streak of iron in the frail old lawyer. 'They have value and would be part of the estate, and I have to administer the estate.'

'I don't see the point,' Marco said. 'I'm his only relative.'

'That's something we must be sure of.' The old lawyer jerked a hand at the painting on the easel. 'Why are you so certain this is your brother's work?'

Marco put down his glass 'Sergio de Castro, the dealer, knew his work and he never questioned it's authenticity.'

'Is he good, this chap De Castro?' Pugh asked.

'Best there is. Very important.'

'Italy's full of a thousand years of the rubbish of

artists,' old Tassinari said quietly. 'There's plenty of work for such as he.'

'And if he says it's a Detto Banti,' Marco pointed out, 'you can accept it without question.'

'We ought to talk to him,' Pugh said. 'Find out if he knows anything of the provenance.'

'There's nothing wrong with the provenance,' Marco said irritably.

'Marco' – the old lawyer spoke quietly but with a soft determination – 'I'm not an art expert. Only an amateur. But I know a little about art and have studied its history and done a little detective work here and there. And as a lawyer who's looked after your brother's interests for a long time, I have to be sure. Twelve Detto Bantis turning up in the cellar here after he's dead, when nobody had ever heard of them—' He shrugged.

'They must have been there for some time,' Marco said.

'Then why didn't the old woman who looked after him know about them? She has a room in the basement, I believe.'

'And she hardly ever went beyond it. Especially in the last years. She grew so bad on her legs.'

'But *you* knew about them. Why didn't *you* sell them to raise money?'

'That's just the point.' Marco gestured with the wine bottle. 'I didn't know about them. I saw those boxes down there – the crates that had been used to send his work to Rome. I thought they were empty.'

Pugh took a sip of the wine and stared again at the canvas on the easel. It was a colourful scene, an allegorical painting of a peasant appealing for help with his arms outspread. Behind him there was a gaunt tree, stark and broken, its two main branches falling coincidentally behind the outstretched arms so that the man looked crucified. Around him soldiers and officials appeared to be jeering at his appeals for help.

'It's called *The Christ of Calabria*,' Marco said.

Pugh's eyes moved across the canvas, noting the light and shade and the way the shafts fell across the central figure. Then he scratched carefully with his fingernail at the scarlet slash of the signature – 'B. Detto Banti'. The painting had a heroic force, but Avvocato Tassinari studied it doubtfully.

'It has the Detto Banti green,' he said slowly. 'His own special colour. I know nobody else had the secret of that green. He told me so. It died with him. And there's that seated figure in the background there, something he always had in his paintings. Yet the red's wrong and there are figures that Bocco would never have painted.'

'He'd have painted anything at the end,' Marco pointed out. 'He settled for simplicity.'

'*When* did he paint it?' Pugh asked.

Marco had disappeared behind the easel and Pugh knew he was unobtrusively slipping a tot of brandy into his wine. He'd noticed him do it before.

'Any time in the three years before he died.' The voice came back firmly from behind the easel.

'It's a bit indifferent for a Detto Banti.'

There was a deep chuckle from behind the easel. 'He was probably drunk.'

Pugh stared at the picture again. 'But why?' he asked.

'Because he often was.'

'Not that. Why paint it and then hide it?'

Marco shrugged. 'It was dangerous. He must have painted it in his anti-Mussolini period. He went through one towards the end. Perhaps that's why he never allowed it to be seen. Under the Fascists, for the sort of sentiment you see there you could be sent to prison.'

Pugh gestured at the other paintings propped up around the studio. In his dedicated way, Tassinari had made a list and they began to discuss them.

'*The Stolen Embrace*,' Tassinari said. '*Washerwoman at a Stream. Funeral at Novara*. That seems to be a scene from one of the battles of the Risorgimento. The character in the middle could well be Garibaldi. *Self-portrait*. It's very like that famous photograph of Bocco that was always used. I think he copied it to save work.'

'He was a bit sly at times,' Marco agreed.

'*The March on Rome,*' Tassinari continued. 'Perhaps that was painted to please Mussolini. I shouldn't imagine it did, though. He looks too soulful and Mussolini never liked to be thought soulful. He liked to be thought of as a man of action. *Meeting of Garibaldi and Vittorio Emmanuelo.*' He stared for a moment. 'Well, it's different from the popular one. *Three Sisters.* The one in the middle's Xenia Anikina, his mistress. I suspect she posed for the others, too, and Bocco merely added a few touches to make them look different.' Tassinari looked at his list again. '*Still Life with Chessmen.*' He stared at the canvas. 'That's different. Bocco was always good with figures, and the figures in the other five aren't his best. But he was never very interested in still life, yet *that* is good. I wonder why he painted it?'

'Change of mood,' Pugh said. 'Fancied doing something different.'

'The Detto Banti green is there in all of them.'

'Almost,' Pugh said, frowning, 'as if he were trying to make certain nobody had any doubt about who painted them. 'Look,' he's saying. "This is Detto Banti colour, clear proof that I, Bocco Detto Banti, painted it." But there isn't much. Not in any of them. Just a touch.'

'He grew lazy in his old age,' Marco explained. 'I don't think he could be bothered to mix it up.'

Tassinari stared at the picture of the washerwomen. 'It's possible,' he said. 'It looks as if he were tired. The brushwork's poor.' His eye moved on. '*Prince of Peace. Boy with Oranges. Sheep Returning to the Fold.*'

'Twelve of them,' Pugh said. 'Eleven totally without protest. So why hide them? A painter of Bocco Detto Banti's standing doesn't do a thing like that.'

Marco shrugged, 'Perhaps he didn't like the thought that when he died there'd be no more of him. Perhaps it was his way of making sure his fame didn't die too soon.'

He sipped at his wine. 'He was fighting a losing battle, of course. He was too pompous. A hundred years from now he'll be lumped with all the others who used to be popular and now won't fetch their weight in beans.'

Pugh stared again at the picture on the easel then he moved across the room and studied the others. '*None* of these are very good Detto Bantis.'

Marco shrugged. 'They're the best we've got and his name's on them.'

As he swallowed what was left of his wine and left the room to find another bottle, Avvocato Tassinari stared at the canvas. 'Marco was always a *truffatore* – a shyster,' he said. 'In a way, they both were. Bocco's trouble was women, Marco's drink. But he's likable enough, you understand, even if you can't trust him. I've been listening to his comments for twenty-four hours now. I knew there was never much love lost between them.' He studied the canvas, frowning, 'Bocco was fashionable, and in his time and at his best he didn't fall *far* short of brilliance.'

Pugh stared again at the painting on the easel. He'd seen plenty of Detto Bantis before the war and somehow this painting looked out of phase. It didn't seem to have Bocco's inherent pomposity – Marco was right about that, he had to admit.

As Marco returned with a fresh bottle, Pugh turned to him. 'Let's have it again,' he said. 'Where they came from, I mean.'

Marco smiled. 'He had his studio here ever since he returned to Italy,' he explained. 'I worked for him. I had to.' He gestured with his glass. 'Because of this. But he became difficult and I left. But then he grew old and dotty and I came back to look after him. Italians believe in family. For seven years I was here, and when I knew he was going to die I started looking round the place for something that might reward me for my care and attention. When I found the canvasses in the cellar I couldn't believe my luck.'

'Why didn't you tell me about them before?' Tassinari asked.

Marco grinned. 'I thought they'd be claimed to pay his debts. He had a few.'

Pugh was studying Marco. 'It's a pity he didn't make a will,' he said.

'Why should he? There's only me. There are no children. When his first wife died childless, he married that model of his, Xenia Anikina, who'd been his mistress for years. But she was a lunatic and he soon kicked her out. She married a Frenchman just after World War I and was killed in a car crash outside Paris in 1922.'

Pugh indicated the canvasses round the room. 'Assuming they're genuine,' he asked, 'how much are they worth?'

'In England, £10,000 each.'

Avvocato Tassinari pulled a face. 'At the present rate of exchange that would be about right,' he agreed. 'Four million lire would not be very wrong. But they would have to be sold quickly. Their price won't improve with age.'

Marco smiled. 'I don't mind,' he said. 'I'll be glad to shuffle him off. I was always the little brother who couldn't paint. In fact, I could paint rings round him.'

'Did you sell much?' Pugh asked.

Marco grinned and gestured with the bottle. 'I never finished much,' he admitted. 'When I came back here Bocco was at the stage when he was glad of help, and when he was too busy, too bored or too drunk, I painted in things like the curtains and the sky for him. You know the green seat in the painting he did of the garden here? The well-known one – *Italian Landscape with Figures*. That was mine.'

Pugh's eyes met the old lawyer's. Then he glanced at the canvas again. Marco smiled.

'You needn't worry,' he encouraged them. 'These are solid parish church Bocco. And at four million lire each, it makes me a wealthy man, doesn't it? I've been fighting off people who wanted to grab them ever since I discovered them. The first to arrive was Sansovino, the Mayor. He said they ought to be stored in the vaults of the Palazzo Municipale. For safety.'

'Why weren't they?'

Marco grinned. 'Because Sansovino's a crook. He was appointed by AMGOT, to take the place of the Fascist *podesta*. If I'd let him have them he'd have bolted with the lot. I've been expecting him to arrive with one of his strong-arm boys to collect them ever since Bocco died. I'm glad I've got somebody here now with a gun and the military authority to make sure I keep them.'

'What does this Sansovino look like?' Pugh asked. 'It might be as well to be able to recognise him.'

Marco pointed across the square. A large, fat man dressed like something out of a Hollywood film – dark shirt, white tie, pin-striped suit and spats – stood with his back to them on the steps of the Palazzo Municipale. Beyond him were three other men, all similarly dressed, and they were talking to an American officer, the fat man's arms waving in good southern Italian gestures.

'That's him,' Marco said. 'The one in front. The officer's taking hand-outs from him. I'll be glad to see the paintings out of their reach, and their value in money in my pocket.'

'They have to be sold first,' Tassinari reminded him.

'They'll sell.' Marco sounded confident. 'When the Germans were here they bought everything he had. They loved them. Particularly the fleshy women he sometimes painted.'

'These won't be going to flesh-loving Germans. They would be sold in an international market where there would be shrewd buyers.'

'They'll still sell. There are plenty of idiots who like to have something to talk about during dinner and they'll pay for the privilege of a story. A newly discovered Detto Banti? They'll pay.'

Pugh had to admit Marco was probably right.

Marco finished off his glass at a gulp. 'It would make him turn in his grave,' he said, 'to think his money was coming to me.'

As they talked they heard the local bus pulling up in the road outside. It was a battered vehicle running on gas and it had smooth tyres and was down at one side where a spring had gone. For a long time Vicinamontane hadn't had a bus and only now, with the front line pushed to the north, had the Allies allowed it to start again. The passengers who descended were mostly townspeople, but among them was a young woman who headed straight for the Ca' di Leone.

'Someone from De Castro, I expect,' Marco said. 'Come about the pictures.'

The girl was fair-haired and blue-eyed like a Florentine, and her clothes were old but good. Like everybody else in Italy she looked as if a hearty meal would help. They waited for the ancient housekeeper to show her into the studio and they were all three standing near the painting when the door opened. The girl smiled nervously at them.

'You're from the De Castro Galleries?' Marco asked.

'How did you know?' Did they telephone?'

'You must be good to work for De Castro.'

She stared at them, her brows wrinkled, then she smiled. 'I think there must be some mistake,' she said, 'I don't *work* for De Castro. I was just directed here by them. I remembered reading that he acted for my father.'

Marco's glass fell to the floor. He kicked the fragments from his feet. 'For a moment,' he managed, 'I thought you said "my father".'

The girl turned to him, looking like a figure from a painting by one of the Florentine School. 'I did,' she agreed. 'I'm Tamara Detto Banti. I'm Boccaccio Detto Banti's daughter, and when I saw he'd died I thought there might be a small painting I could have. Since there's nobody else, I suppose I could.' She studied them. '*Non è vero*? Surely that's so?'

58

5

You could have cut the atmosphere in the big studio with a knife. Marco Detto Banti had fled at once to the brandy bottle and at the moment he was making no attempt to hide it with wine. Only the girl was happily unaware of what was going on, her neat head turning from one to the other.

'I saw an expert,' she said. 'He was busy trying to date me so I thought I might as well pick his brains a little. He said I ought to come here. He said even pencil sketches by someone like my father would be valuable. He understands the *belli arti* and he's dealt with paintings before, so he knew what he was talking about. I took a few days off from my job at the hospital to come.'

'Who was this expert?' Pugh asked. 'This man who told you to come here?'

'He was an American officer,' she said cheerfully. 'In the legal department of their army. In Naples. I met him at the hospital.'

Pugh wondered why *he'd* never met her, because he'd always made a point of meeting every pretty girl he saw and he wasn't unknown at the hospital.

'And it was in Naples you learned your father was dead?' Tassinari asked.

'I read it in the paper. They said he was English. But he wasn't. He was Italian.'

'That's a matter of opinion,' Pugh said. 'Did you know him?'

'I never met him in my life. My mother never got on with him. Particularly when she remarried. *Non c'è un vero grande amore.* And after all, he made no provision for her. There was just no contact at all.'

'What about you? Why didn't you ever meet him?'

'Xenia didn't like babies. She hadn't expected one and when I arrived she made a point of getting rid of me as soon as possible. I was placed in the care of an old couple called Dulcecuore in Caserta. They brought me up and, I suspect, did a better job of it than she would have. I owe them everything – affection, common sense, help. They both died in 1939 and I never thought much about my father until I saw in the paper that he was dead. I knew he had no other children and I thought I'd like one of his paintings – as much for sentimental reasons as anything – and I got the address. Signor de Castro didn't seem very eager to give it to me.'

Probably he was hoping to collar the paintings himself, Pugh thought. He had seen enough of liberated Italy by this time to be suspicious of everybody.

'In the end I got it in a sort of backhanded way from one of his typists,' Tamara Detto Banti went on.

Pugh indicated Marco, who was gulping at a fresh glass. 'This,' he said, 'is Marco Detto Banti. He's your father's younger brother.'

'I didn't know he had one.'

Pugh glanced at his watch. 'Until about three minutes ago,' he thought *he* was the heir.'

The girl stared at Marco. 'Oh, Madonna,' she said. 'I'm terribly sorry. Can't we come to some arrangement?' She stared at the canvas. 'Is that one of my father's paintings?'

'Yes.'

She frowned. 'You know, as a matter of fact, I don't particularly like Detto Bantis.' She looked at Pugh. 'Do *you* like Detto Bantis?' she asked.

'I'm not here to like or dislike,' Pugh said. He was there to collect them for the British Government – or Colonel Tasker. Perhaps even for Colonel Baracca. Now, he thought gleefully, neither looked like getting them. The British Government's loss left him cold. Governments could handle that sort of thing. But Tasker's loss delighted him.

The girl was still staring at the painting on the easel, her brows wrinkled, and she didn't seem to hear what he said. 'And after all,' she pointed out, 'he wasn't very popular, was he?'

'His canvasses will still fetch four million lire.'

She looked startled. 'That much?'

'That much.'

She brushed her hair out of her eyes and stared hard at Pugh.

'Who are you?' she asked. 'What's your interest?'

'This,' Tassinari said, 'is Sergeant Pugh. He is an English soldier.'

She sniffed. 'What has he to do with it?'

'He has come to collect the paintings.'

She gave Pugh an old-fashioned look. 'I'm sure,' she said. 'That is what soldiers do. Collect *everything*.'

'I might even find a buyer for you,' Pugh said shortly. 'I'm trying to help.'

'Soldiers are *always* trying to help Italian girls.'

'They happen to like them.'

'I'm not so sure the girls like the soldiers. They're arrogant and loud and stupid. They boast too much. And you bombed our cities.'

'The Germans happened to be in them.'

'And now we have the British and the Americans instead.' Her anger boiled over. 'Why does nobody listen to us? You tell us what to do but you never ask what we think! You're so busy telling us to be your allies because it's good for Italy, but logic doesn't make converts. A few shiploads of food would win us over much more quickly than politics.'

Tassinari smiled. 'Nobody,' he said, 'can love the unwanted guest in his house, whether he's a friend or an enemy.'

Pugh shrugged. He could understand her bitterness, especially since the Allies didn't always seem to be very allied. The British envied the Americans and despised the Canadians; the Canadians hated the British and envied the Americans; the French sneered at the British and shook their heads in disbelief at the Americans; the Americans just felt sorry for everybody. In addition, pedestrians were killed with monotonous regularity on every corner by military vehicles that were too big and too heavy for the small towns through which they were driven with total indifference by their drivers. There always seemed to be someone dead or dying in the gutter, covered with a blanket or a coat until the ambulance or the carabinieri came to take them away. Since there were no medicines in the hospitals, they were even considered lucky if they died en route, while the blood remained as a warning in a thick pool in the gutter.

Tamara Detto Banti was still studying Pugh with great suspicion, 'If you're a soldier, what do you know about painting?'

'I used to be a painter, too. Here. In Italy. I even met Boccaccio Detto Banti.'

'You did?' Her eyes lit up and she forgot her suspicion at once. 'What was he like?'

'Pretty old at the time.'

Her suspicion seemed to recede and she looked at him with more interest.

'Are they really worth a lot of money?'

Pugh shrugged. 'Well, they're not very good for Detto Bantis.'

'They're Detto Bantis all right.' The voice came from behind the easel in a choking quaver.

Tassinari joined in. 'Shall we say, Signorina, that they're different and that might affect their price? Bocco Detto Banti was never an inspired painter but he was a craftsman. He had great skill and a lot of knowledge. So, if they *are* Detto Bantis I imagine they'd fetch roughly what we suggest.'

'*Madonna mia!*' She seemed awed. 'You said, "*they'd* fetch". Are there any more?'

Pugh gestured at the paintings propped up around the room. 'Twelve altogether.'

She did a quick mental calculation and her face fell. '*Mamma mia*,' she said, 'that's 48 million lire!'

'*Precisamente*,' Avvocato Tassinari said dryly. 'Exactly.'

She stared at them, obviously a little shaken. '48 million lire!' She turned to Marco, who had hardly said a word since she'd appeared. 'I seem to have put my foot in it, don't I?'

Marco waved a hand, still speechless.

'I expect we can come to some arrangement,' she repeated, with a disarming willingness to share. She gazed at the canvas on the easel again. 'Do you really think it would fetch that much?' she asked.

Avvocato Tassinari nodded. 'A Detto Banti would fetch four million lire anywhere. A good one might even fetch five or six. People buy paintings these days as investments.'

'Bocco would be a lousy insurance,' Marco growled.

Tassinari smiled. 'That's something we don't tell eager buyers.'

'I'm only organising them, of course,' he went on. 'I don't fix the price. That comes from the state of supply and demand, and the supply of Detto Bantis is limited, while the supply of unknowns isn't.'

'And if they aren't Detto Bantis?'

Pugh studied the pictures. 'The lot – 120,000 lire. That's all, and that's not much.'

She looked at Marco with an expression that was a cross between pity and an apology. 'We had better take our pick, you and I, I think,' she said.

'There's no question of him taking his pick,' Tassinari pointed out. 'If you're who you say you are, in the eyes of the law the paintings are yours. *All of them.*'

The man behind the easel choked and, as they turned towards him, he turned away, his eyes streaming, a hand waving to indicate he didn't need assistance. The door slammed.

'Poor man,' Tamara Detto Banti said. 'Did he really think they were his?'

Pugh nodded. 'I think he'd got his life mapped out to the grave on the strength of them.'

'Can't we share them?'

Tassinari shrugged. 'There's nothing to stop you giving away your own property, of course, Signorina,' he said. 'But it isn't as easy as all that. The law takes its time.'

'I wouldn't dream of beggaring him! I never met my father, of course, and I know nothing of him. But if there are that many, I wouldn't miss one or two, would I? Couldn't I arrange not to have them? My friend said I could do what I liked with them, and he's a lawyer.'

'As it happens,' Tassinari said gravely, 'so am I.'

'Oh!' She stared at him. 'I thought you were a dealer or something.' She stared at the canvas again. 'But 48 million lire. *Dio mio*, I don't want *that* much! I'd only waste it.'

'Not if you were well advised.'

She seemed a little unnerved. 'One picture would do.' She gestured at the easel. 'That one. That's all I expected. I'd settle for four million any time. Less. He could keep the rest.'

'Unfortunately,' Pugh said, 'they're not his to keep. If a man finds a piece of jewellery in the street he's not entitled to sell it as his own. When your uncle found these canvasses, he *seemed* to have the right to them as the nearest relative. Now it seems he's suddenly lost that right. You could always reward him for finding them, of course.'

'Can't I give them away then? To my uncle.'

'It becomes you, Signorina,' Tassinari said, 'but I'd suggest not immediately. And if you'll accept my advice, which I'll offer you, in a most unlawyer-like way, for nothing. I'd wait until we've established that they *are* Detto Bantis.'

'And assuming they are?'

Pugh glanced at the easel. 'It could start a run on Detto Bantis,' he said. 'Because there haven't been any

64

for a long time and, with damage, looting and theft by the Germans, there's a great shortage of pictures. When the war ends, art treasures of any kind will be in great demand and a lot of people will be looking for them. Twelve at once could start a fashion. However, these were painted in a hurry – perhaps even with that in mind. Or else under difficult conditions – perhaps because the Germans were here, perhaps because he needed the money and then it was found there was no movement in art sales so he couldn't get rid of them and had to stick them in the cellar until times were better. I would suggest releasing one of the best ones to stir up interest and let buyers think about it for a while.'

The girl frowned. 'You're sure you're not a dealer? You think like one. How long would it take?'

'The law doesn't move fast,' Tassinari said. 'The first thing is to get them to where they can be appraised. They certainly oughtn't to remain here.'

'I could arrange for money to be advanced,' Pugh said, knowing even Tasker ought to be willing to cough up something to make sure he got his mitts on his loot. 'This, of course, is providing you can establish your identity.'

She looked contemptuous. 'The law *is* stuffy, isn't it?'

Tassinari shrugged. 'The law doesn't take chances,' he reminded her. 'That's why it's the law.'

She seemed to be vaguely hostile, as though she resented their opposition to her offer to help Marco. '*Allora*,' she said. 'It so happens I have all my mother's papers, including the registrations of her marriage and my birth. They all came to me when she died. I kept them. I was proud of being Boccaccio Detto Banti's daughter, you see.'

Tassinari smiled at Pugh. 'A clever one, this, *non è vero?*' he said. 'She reminds me of my daughter who died in 1937.' He spread his hands as if to exhibit signs of the stigmata. 'Her documents appear to be sound, too. I wonder if we can get her lawyer friend to act for her.'

Tamara looked him straight in the eye. 'No,' she said. 'You can't. The night before I came here, I found he'd been taking a girl friend of mine to bed.'

Pugh decided that with Tamara Detto Banti around, the lawyer friend must have been a nutcase.

'If it's any help,' he said, 'I'll do what I can.'

'You don't have to,' she said stiffly.

'I know I don't have to. But it seems there's a lot to clear up and it might be as well.'

'Because it'll help you? Not because it'll help me?'

'The law's stuffy,' Pugh reminded her. 'You said so yourself. It doesn't make a habit of doing things for people just because their eyes are blue or because they have a nice smile.'

She looked pleased. 'Have I?' she said.

6

Tamara Detto Banti sat opposite Pugh at a table in the little restaurant in the main square of Vicinamontane. There were a few restaurants open, but the place had been swept too often by the hand of war and all they seemed able to offer was soup made out of God alone knew what part of a chicken, and rissoles made from black market British army corned beef. But there was a Camaldoli wine from the slopes of Vesuvius which, if it was rough, was still wine.

Avvocato Tassinari, worn out by the toils of the day, had decided to rest, while Marco Detto Banti was well drunk by this time. Since there was no sign of the old help, Enrichetta, Pugh had suggested eating out.

'My father married Xenia after the last war,' Tamara was saying. 'He served in the Italian army, but he had lived in England up to 1914 and he went to Paris after the war. It was then that he met Xenia, who was a refugee from the Russian revolution. She left him in 1920, by which time he was in England again. He left there in 1934 to return to Italy.'

'Have you no other relations?' Pugh asked.

'No.'

'You're not married?'

She frowned. 'My *fidanzato* went into the army and was killed in the winter of 1940/41.' She looked as if she had a world of sorrow on her shoulders. 'His family sent his belongings to me. I realise now I didn't know him very well.' She paused. 'And now, after three years, I can hardly remember what he looked like. I took refuge in work. I am a *segretaria privata* at the hospital in Naples.

67

Technical assistant, you would say, I think. To Signor Finzi, the surgeon. Very special. With much knowledge, because I was once a nurse.'

Pugh had met a few secretaries and nurses in Naples. Some of them would sleep with anyone for a meal, but he didn't think this one would.

She was gazing at Pugh in a way that started up all his old ambitions, and an unexpected itch to paint the smooth curve of her cheek. With her fair hair, short upper lip and green eyes, she reminded him of one of Botticelli's goddesses or Bronzino's portrait of Lucrezia Panciatichi.

'Sergeant,' she went on after a long silence, 'I think you and I are going to see a lot of each other because of these pictures of my father's.'

'That seems likely,' Pugh agreed, not at all alarmed by the prospect. Her face was full of character, and when she allowed herself to smile it seemed to take over and made her a different person altogether.

'Well,' she said, 'I can't go on for ever calling you Sergeant Pugh.' She pronounced it Poo. 'It is such a silly name. No Italian would have a name like that. What is your Christian name?'

'Tom.'

'Tomaso,' she said. 'That is a good Italian name.'

'Not Tomaso – Tom.'

'That is what I said. A good Italian name.'

'There's another. Wooster. Thomas Wooster Pugh.'

'She looked up. 'Oo-ooster?' She made it sound like a train going through a tunnel. 'This is surely not for true?' She gave an unexpected grin. 'Under the circumstances I had better go on calling you Sergeant Poo. In Florence, where I came from, we do not stand on ceremony much. And, since you say you are an avvocato also, perhaps I ought to call you Avvocato Poo.' She considered it. 'But perhaps not,' she decided. 'It is too difficult.' She frowned. 'If you are an avvocato, why do you not practise as one?'

'My wife ran away with the junior partner. I decided to throw it up and paint.'

'And you made a success of it?'

'On the contrary. I made a failure.'

'And this is why you are only a sergeant? In the Italian army an avvocato would become an officer.'

'He would in the British army, too, but I blotted my copybook.'

'By becoming an artist?'

'The Law Society doesn't approve of bohemian types with long hair and red ties. They prefer stiff collars, dark suits and frozen faces. They'll probably make me an officer later if I purge myself of my contempt by promising not to be a painter after the war.'

She gave a little giggle. 'Will you?'

'I think it would be more sensible. While starving as a painter I noticed that my friends – all lawyers, some of them very bad ones, too – rarely went hungry. Obesity, in fact, can be an occupational hazard among lawyers.'

She looked sympathetic. 'I understand,' she said. 'It is good to be a painter. Very *simpatico*. But' – she paused – 'that is head logic, and perhaps it is better to be a lawyer, which is stomach logic. Money is important. Especially to Italians.'

He agreed. 'It's occurred to me several times that, with the mess the war's caused, when it's over there's going to be a great need for lawyers – and there's one thing lawyers always make sure of and that is that they're not poor.'

She studied him carefully, realising that with his strong features and crisp dark hair he was better-looking than she had thought. 'Is this true why they didn't make you an officer?' she asked.

'Not really. I didn't go to Oxford or Cambridge, so I wasn't considered an okay type.'

'An okay type?'

'Gentlemanly – *cavalleresco, signorile*. Also, the officer who interviewed me was a pansy.'

'Come?'

'*Omosessuale*. He liked fair-haired, slender young men with smooth cheeks.'

'But this is not a very important job for a man as clever as you.'

'The only alternative was giving dull lectures on security to sullen soldiers who didn't want to listen. So I volunteered for overseas because I met a man who'd just come home from Africa and he said overseas was more fun than at home. He was right. It is.'

She studied him again, deciding the British army was full of madmen. 'I think they do not appreciate you,' she said firmly.

'I think the same.'

'I also think you are a rebel.'

He grinned. 'When the war's over, I shall never polish my shoes or call any man "sir" again as long as I live.'

A patrol went past outside, heavily armed, and another group of soldiers was piling stores not far away. They worked slowly as though they resented the work. But, in the restaurant, no one even bothered to watch them and the elderly waiters moved between the tables as though it were just a normal day.

Tamara Detto Banti pushed at her corned beef rissole for a while then she looked up at Pugh.

'You know,' she said, 'I keep thinking about those paintings and what they're worth. Forty-eight million lire!'

'You'd need a good lawyer.'

She gave him a sharp look. 'I've finished with lawyers for the moment,' she said. 'I thought he wanted to marry me.'

'Some lawyers work for their clients without wanting to marry them,' Pugh pointed out.

'Yes' – she considered for a moment – 'but 48 million lire! It frightens me.'

'You could get used to it.'

She pushed at the corned beef again. 'When I came

here,' she said thoughtfully, 'I thought I might perhaps get a few thousand. I never realised there were all these paintings in existence.'

Pugh toyed with the stem of his glass. 'Let's not overestimate at the moment,' he said. 'Or, for that matter, underestimate. I've got a disbelieving nature and I think your uncle's been bilking your father for years. I don't think he's stopped now he's dead, either.'

'That is a very cruel thing to say.'

'It's the way lawyers think. It's also the way Intelligence sergeants think. Both are naturally suspicious. There ought to be drawings – pencil sketches, that sort of thing. But there aren't, and I suspect Marco has them somewhere. *They'd* be worth money too. And there ought to be one or two other canvasses. I'm surprised there aren't any half-finished ones. I suspect Marco's got rid of those also.'

'He wouldn't do that!'

Pugh smiled. 'That's not the opinion of Avvocato Tassinari,' he said. 'And he knew them both for years. If we could establish where they are, we could claim them and that would push up the value of the estate a bit more.'

Her face fell. 'I feel so mean,' she said. 'Especially as Marco planned on it all being his.'

'I shouldn't worry too much about Marco,' Pugh said. 'Marco knows how to look after himself.'

'But he seemed to be making plans.'

'You should never make plans before the law's had its say,' Pugh said. 'That's why I'm advising you not to be too certain. We have to establish the genuineness of the canvases first.'

'Who else would have painted them?'

'Pupils. It happens. And your father had a few from time to time.'

'But his name's on them.'

'An unscrupulous dealer wouldn't hesitate to put it there.'

She stared at him. 'You know,' she observed, 'I'm sure you're not really as unpleasant as you seem to be. But you are being very cruel to Marco. Don't you trust him?'

Pugh smiled. 'Your father was known for his lack of concentration in his later years,' he said.

Marco still looked shaken when they returned to the house. He had been at the brandy bottle again and had a murderous look in his eye. When Pugh asked about the arrangements for the packing and transportation of the newly discovered Detto Bantis, he remained totally indifferent.

'You've changed a bit,' Pugh observed.

'I thought I was going to get something for them,' Marco answered sullenly.

'I'm sure we could come to some arrangement.' Tamara was still faintly apologetic.

'Come to some arrangement!' Marco said explosively in English. 'After all the work I wasted on the goddam things!'

He stood staring at the pictures for some time and was just about to disappear to the bottle again when Tamara turned to Pugh.

'Let me make this clear, Sergeant Poo,' she pointed out. 'I'm not going to take *all* these pictures.'

'You ought to think it over seriously,' Pugh said.

'I've thought it over. I've been thinking it over all evening. I can split 48 million lire down the middle without missing it.'

'Suppose they're not genuine,' Pugh said. 'Then you'd be splitting a few thousand, which doesn't leave you a lot.'

There was silence for a moment as this information was digested, then Marco appeared from behind the easel, still holding the brandy bottle, which he made no attempt to hide.

'They're genuine,' he said abruptly.

'All this is wasting time,' Tamara pointed out. 'I want to share them.'

72

'Down the middle?' Marco asked, and her eyes flickered to Pugh.

'You can do what you like with your own property,' Pugh said. 'But down the middle sounds a bit over-generous to me. If you insist, I should suggest a portion.'

'How much?'

'One-tenth.'

'One-tenth?' Marco's face flushed angrily.

'That's 4,800,000 lire. That's not a bad gift, especially since it doesn't *have* to be made.'

The night was windless and they could smell the damp in the air as lorries kept pounding past the house out of the town.

Marco seemed to recover a little of his good temper, as though he'd decided finally that one-tenth of the value of his brother's paintings was better than nothing, and he entered into the discussion about getting them packed – if not with enthusiasm, then at least without hostility.

'I might keep one.' Tamara was staring thoughtfully at the canvasses. 'For myself. After all he was my father.'

Tassinari frowned his disapproval and she went on defiantly. 'Sometimes, people do things for other reasons than money.'

'I'd get rid of them,' Marco said. 'Quickly. Values change and the value of these will not go up.'

'I'll still keep one.'

Marco gave them a last drink. He was in a better temper but by this time he was also very drunk.

The house was full of the rubbish accumulated by two elderly men over a long time, and the spare bedrooms were a mass of junk. Pugh gave up the bed he'd been allotted to Tamara and was dossing down in the studio in a shambles of lay figures, costumes, models and hats. As he undressed, he was still thinking about the estate. Like Tassinari, he was puzzled at the absence of any pencil sketches. There was nothing of any value beyond

73

the paintings and he was sure Marco had extracted a few things here and there to be sold privately. They'd probably never find them now, but under the circumstances perhaps it was fair enough, even if it wasn't very legal. Whatever Marco could get for them could help soothe his injured spirit, and pay for his years of work, and somehow he had a feeling that Tamara wouldn't object. She was too soft-hearted by a long shot.

It rained hard for the funeral. Boccaccio Detto Banti, who had been lying in state in his bedroom, finally had the lid of the coffin placed over him and screwed down.

The undertaker, a thin man called Ciasca with a lugubrious face that seemed to have been expressly designed to fit his profession, was dressed in a black frock coat turning green with age, and the hearse was of funereal black, chipped and scarred here and there but decorated with chromium-plate polished with British army Brasso. Huge foliated lanterns at the corner reflected the dim grey day as the cherubs, death's heads, extinguished torches and weeping angels dripped water. One of the glass panels was cracked and the black and silver curtains inside had a tatty, faded look about them. The horse was so old it seemed as if it were about to drop dead at any moment.

Because of the possibility of a German counterattack, Ciasca was eager to get the business over and done with, but he had been unable to obtain mutes to carry the coffin and in the end Pugh allowed himself to be roped in with Marco. With the undertaker and the one attendant he had managed to raise, they brought the coffin unsteadily downstairs, Pugh hoping to God he wouldn't trip and fall and bring the lot down after him. The crucifix on the lid was loose and was hanging upside down, and Pugh thought the body must have shifted because the whole weight on the coffin seemed to be on his shoulder.

'Easy now,' Ciasca warned.

'What if the horse moves?' Pugh asked.

'Fiorello will never move,' Ciasca said. 'He hasn't the strength or the youth. And that is good and the reason why horse hearses are always best. Motor hearses are faster, but arriving with a shriek of brakes and a cloud of dust doesn't add decorum to a funeral. This is a taxing profession, Signore, and one I have never liked, but if there's one thing I can rely on it is that Fiorello will not move. Sometimes he doesn't move even when I wish him to.'

The priest looked as old as Avvocato Tassinari and just as fragile and uncertain of his feet, and the two old men seemed to support each other into the cemetery. There were no followers except Tamara, Enrichetta from the kitchen, muttering under a black shawl, and two small boys and a dog who were there purely out of curiosity. Bocco Detto Banti had outlived most of his contemporaries, and those who were still around had obviously considered it would do them no good to get soaked. Instead of the funeral of a man whose name had once been lionised both in London and Rome, it looked more like the funeral of a small Neapolitan business-man.

'All that is missing, Poo,' Tamara said, 'is the uncle from Rome.'

'Who's that?'

'It's not a who, it's a what.'

Tassinari explained. 'Families in the south are always concerned with pride. A man in Naples who has lived all his life close to poverty still has to be buried with a show of histrionics, which includes an expensive coffin, flowers and an "uncle from Rome".'

'They hire them from an agency,' Tamara said. 'A distinguished old man who can produce a Roman accent and knows not to use his hands when he talks. He arrives either by train or in a well-polished car with a Rome number plate. The qualifications are a patrician manner and the ability to address strangers in the old-

75

fashioned way. It brings dignity to the occasion and tempers the grief of the Neapolitans.'

Tassinari coughed. 'I have not been above acting the uncle from Rome when I have been short of money,' he said. 'Particularly as I have the ribbon of a Commendatore of the Crown of Italy. It was my father's. It always adds to the occasion.'

Tamara nodded understandingly and looked at the disbelieving Pugh. 'Sometimes, Poo,' she said, 'when you are frowning, I think it would be a profession at which you would do well.' She pulled a face. 'Unfortunately, with the battle front between us and Rome, it is not possible. I imagine a lot of Roman uncles are having a thin time just now.'

Waiting by the cemetery gate was a black car, from which stepped three men – Sansovino, the Mayor, and two of his bodyguards, obviously there because Sansovino considered it his duty to pay homage to Vicinamontane's best-known inhabitant. For the first time, Pugh got a good look at him.

'I've seen him before,' he said to Tamara. In the Poggio Reale prison, he thought, frowning, just leaving after a visit to Tirandolo, the man he'd arrested for smuggling drugs.

The cemetery was behind an enclosed wall and consisted of the usual shelves and numbered niches where the dead were stacked like a giant filing cabinet, and though there was no family tomb, Bocco had thriftily bought his place years before. Only half aware of the priest's monotonous chant, Avvocato Tassinari swaying on his feet and Enrichetta's angry muttering, Pugh found himself staring at Tamara Detto Banti. Like many Italian girls, she was small, but she had good legs and, though her nose was long in the Italian manner, it was well proportioned and her eyes were large and her hair the bronze of so many Florentines

She didn't notice he was looking at her, but she was thinking about him. She wasn't sure she could trust him, but she also had a feeling that she could probably trust him a great deal more than her uncle who stood alongside him, short, dark-haired, more like a gardener in a convent than anything else.

As they left the cemetery, Pugh noticed that Ciasca, the undertaker, was quietly placing the flowers that had arrived to one side. When everybody had disappeared, he was sure, so would the flowers. Ciasca had confided in an aside that there was another funeral the following day and Pugh knew he would see no sense in leaving them to be stolen by someone else – probably to be made into a bride's bouquet – when they could be used again the next morning. The last he saw of him was surreptitiously pushing the flowers into the back of the hearse as they left, while the scraggy, broken-kneed horse waited, head down, the rain dripping off its coat.

When they returned to the house, all of them soaked, Enrichetta produced the small meal she had left ready. It consisted of a quiche made out of crushed British army biscuits, cheese, a single egg she had begged from the nearby farm, lumps of what looked like black pudding made from pig's blood, and pieces of bully beef – like the biscuits, obtained from British army rations. Only the wine was worth tasting.

Curiously, the town seemed to have emptied and all the lorries that had been in the square had gone. There were no people about either, and Pugh put it down to the weather, the expected German counter-attack, or both. Certainly there were no longer girls with their eyes glued to the windows.

The priest and Ciasca, the undertaker, and his solitary attendant had turned up to see Bocco Detto Banti on his way with a glass of wine, because no one in Italy turned down the chance of food and drink, and Pugh found himself facing the attendant, who was a square, dark man wearing a beard and an Italian army uniform jacket. He was short-legged like most Italian soldiers, and as they talked he introduced himself.

77

'Foscari,' he said, 'Foscari, Enzio. Sergeant. 103rd Regiment.'

He was a polite man, anxious to please and easy to talk to, and he was fascinated by Pugh's accent and the lack of threadbareness in his uniform.

'But you, of course, signore, are of the British army,' he said. 'I am very proud to meet you.'

Wretchedly equipped and armed and totally devoid of comfort, Foscari had had more than he could stand of Mussolini and his heel-clicking generals with their salutes, medals, corruption and inefficiency. He had faithfully resisted all the way back across the North African desert and into Sicily and, when the armistice was declared, he was near Milan, recovering from a wound and acting as guard to a prison camp. On hearing General Eisenhower's announcement, he had simply walked out, intending to return to his wife and family in Naples, where he had hoped to pick up the threads of his life. He did not consider himself a coward; he was simply tired of fighting a useless war for what he had come to accept as a wicked and corrupt government.

'There are too many dead men,' he said. 'And there is always work for an undertaker.' He smiled. 'That was my job before the war, which is why Agente di Pompe Funebri Ciasca employed me. It provides money and food to help me on my way.'

He brought news of British prisoners of war to the north. When the armistice had been arranged, they had received orders to stand fast, but to Foscari the only indication of peace had been painted signs on the wall of the building opposite the camp – ARMISTIZIO and BENITO FINITO – and two hours later he had seen a German column arrive and all the prisoners rounded up.

'I decided I had better leave,' he said.

Having nothing to lose, all the way south the peasants had been helpful, supplying him with clothing, food and, when he needed it, a bed. He had been in the mountains, living in a cave, supplied with food by *carbonari* families

78

who lived by making charcoal, but with the approach of spring he had decided the time had come to make an attempt to reach home.

'What are *you* doing here, your honour?' he asked Pugh.

Pugh explained. 'My job is to get Bocco Detto Banti's pictures to Naples,' he said. 'I have to see them crated and transported.'

Foscari gave him a flashing smile. 'Perhaps I can help,' he said. 'In the army I spent much time making crosses for the graves of dead soldiers. I am good with wood, you see, because undertakers are also carpenters. I will remain behind to help the Signore Sergente.'

As they closed the door on Ciasca and the old priest, Pugh stood for a moment staring out at the grey weather. Enrichetta and Tamara were busy in the kitchen and Tassinari was trying to recover in a chair from the chill of the rain in front of a fire built by Marco from the remains of an old chest he had chopped up. Foscari stood near the stairs, waiting for instructions.

Pugh was just about to turn to him when there was a knock on the door. Opening it, Pugh found himself facing Sansovino, the Mayor, backed by two of his bodyguards. He smiled, his wide rat-trap mouth splitting to show bad teeth. Pugh didn't smile back. Knowing Sansovino had been appointed to his position through friendship with Naples gangsters and corrupt AMGOT officers was bad enough, but he also couldn't forget having seen him leaving the Poggio Reale prison after a visit to Tirandolo. It didn't require much imagination to assume the two were connected and that they were both involved in the rackets. The smile grew wider as Pugh's face grew more frozen.

'I am Sansovino, Vicenzo, Mayor of Vicinamontane.'

'I know.'

Sansovino removed his hat and held it to his chest. 'You are the English sergente who has come to attend to

79

the affairs of Boccaccio Detto Banti,' he said.

'I am.'

'I am here to express my condolences and to assure you at all times of my earnest desire to be of assistance—'

'What do you want?'

The smile disappeared as if cut off by a switch. 'I am approaching you to suggest, with the greatest respect for the Allied armies and their wishes, of course, that the pictures of the late Boccaccio Detto Banti should be placed in the vaults of the Palazzo Municipale. For safe keeping.'

'No,' Pugh snapped.

'I assure you, Signore Sergente—'

'I said no.'

The obsequiousness vanished for a moment. Then it returned. 'I assure the Signore Sergente that I have only the welfare of the Italian nation and its allies, the British and American armies, at heart.'

'The paintings stay where they are.'

Sansovino's mouth closed and his eyes glittered dangerously. 'The Signore Sergente chooses to be stubborn.'

'More than that. Obdurate. They do not go to the Palazzo Municipale.'

'May I ask why not, Sergente?'

'You may. My orders are that they do not.'

Sansovino stood staring at Pugh for a while, and he opened his mouth to ask another question, changed his mind, closed it, and gave a little bow.

'As the Signore Sergente wishes,' he said. 'I trust he will not regret his decision.'

'It isn't my decision. It's my orders.'

Sansovino was all smiles again now and he backed away, still clutching his hat to his chest. The two bodyguards gave Pugh a glare and made way for him. A last bow, then Sansovino was heading back to the Palazzo Municipale.

Pugh watched them go. He had a feeling that Sansovino wasn't finished and that it was going to be necessary to remove the pictures quickly from Vicinamontane before Sansovino took matters into his own hands. Accidents could be arranged easily enough, and the country north of Naples could hardly yet be called 'controlled by the Allies'. Rather it was a vague no man's land where the Allies gave the orders, but the people respected them only if it suited them, because there was still the chance the Germans might return.

He turned to find Foscari still standing near the stairs, his eyes on him.

'Can you work fast?' Pugh asked.

'I am a very good carpenter, Signor Sergente, and when necessary I can work like the wind.'

Pugh nodded. 'Then let's get on with it,' he said.

7

Foscari tossed Marco's hammer down and stretched. Seating himself on one of the nailed-up crates, he stared about him. There was no electricity in the cellar where they had been working and they had struggled in the light of a single lamp powered with nothing stronger than kerosene. Because he didn't trust Marco, Pugh had done the job alone with Foscari, who fancied himself as a singer and had persisted in treating him to his favourite songs as he worked.

'They look good,' Pugh said, studying what they'd done.

'I am moved by a desire for justice, sir, and, like the Signore Sergente, I do not trust men like Vicenze Sansovino.'

Pugh offered a cigarette – an American Camel – and he smiled.

'The sheep with the hump,' he said. 'A cigarette – any cigarette – has become a luxury.' He glanced at the crates. 'The Signore Sergente is worried.'

'I think we should get the pictures away as fast as possible. Too many people seem to be interested in them.'

'Also the Germans might return.' Foscari pulled a face. 'Twelve of them. Madonna. Many lire! Whose are they, Signore?'

'They belong to Signorina Detto Banti.'

Foscari grinned. 'I wish I did,' he said. 'Is she the Sergente's girl, sir?'

'No.' Pugh thought it might be a good idea to look her

up, nevertheless, when he got her safely back to Naples.
'I only met her yesterday.'

'She will be worth much money, I think.'

'She will if the paintings are what we think they are.'

'Does the Signore Sergente think they might not be?'

'I see no reason why they shouldn't be. They're
signed. All she'll have to do is find a buyer.'

Foscari stuffed the hammer into Marco's tool box
where it belonged, with the screwdrivers, jemmy and all
the other necessities for crating pictures. His carpentry
skills had been valuable because even nails and screws
were at a premium and they had had to cannibalise
several of the crates to produce enough material to pack
the twelve pictures. They climbed the stairs to the
ground floor, still talking.

'Does the Signore Sergente expect to get the
paintings to Naples?' Foscari asked.

'The Signore Sergente must. The army will supply a
lorry.'

'And you will be taking everybody down in it, sir?'

'I also have a car.'

'The Sergente should watch it or the wheels will
disappear.'

'I've thought of that.' The car had been locked up
behind the house, well out of sight.

'There are five people, sir.'

'Four.'

'No, Signore. Five. The Signorina. The brother.
Avvocato Tassinari. The Sergente himself. And now
me. I would like a lift. I need to go home.

'I can't accept responsibility for you.'

'I think the Signore Sergente must,' Foscari said.
'Now. It will become uncomfortable for me if the
paintings disappear and I remain behind. Sansovino
knows I am a carpenter because I have made coffins for
Ciasca, the undertaker. He will guess who helped you.'

Pugh said nothing because he suspected Foscari was
right.

83

'There will be the lorry, sir,' Foscari went on. 'Can I not be included as an assistant? I do not take up much room.' He hunched his shoulders and drew his knees together. 'You see? Very small.'

Pugh slapped his shoulders and smiled. 'You make out a good case,' he said.

They were still talking when a car stopped at the door. It was battered-looking, but it was an Italian army car and most Italian army cars were battered-looking, chiefly because the Italian army had neither the money to replace them nor the means to repair them. The man who climbed out of it didn't go with it. He was tall, handsome, and wore a spotless uniform with gleaming top boots and the wide-winged breeches that always seemed to be favoured by the dictator countries.

'Good God,' Pugh said. 'It's Da Sangalla!' He glanced round at Foscari. 'Look, Enzio, I want you to keep quiet about those paintings in the cellar.'

Foscari frowned. 'Is this man a crook, Signore? There are many about.'

'I don't know what he is. But there are already far too many people interested in these paintings. If you're asked, you just don't know. Got it?'

'*Lo capisco*. I have it sir.'

'In the meantime, slip upstairs and tell the others the same. Tassinari won't argue. Neither will Marco. He's too frightened of losing his share. Just explain to Signorina Detto Banti. Okay?'

'Okay, sir.'

Da Sangalla didn't seem surprised as Pugh opened the door. Enrichetta, her work finished, her obligations to the Detto Banti family finished, had expressed her wish to return to her own family in the hills, and Tassinari had paid her off.

'Sergeant Pugh.' Da Sangalla smiled. 'I heard you were here.'

How did he hear, Pugh wondered. Was the bastard working with Tasker? The ramifications of corruption in Italy, and particularly in Naples, were so extensive anything was possible. Da Sangalla was a product of the Fine Arts Department of the University of Florence but defeat led people into strange pathways.

'And I heard *you'd* be here eventually,' Pugh said.

'You know why I've come, of course?'

'Of course.'

'I'm from the Ministero di Monumento e Belle Arti. I'm here to claim the Detto Banti collection for the Italian nation.'

Pugh smiled. 'I represent the Commission for the Protection of Arts and Monuments and that's exactly why I'm here. *I'm* claiming it for the *British* nation.'

Da Sangalla frowned. 'Boccaccio Detto Banti was an Italian.'

'According to London he was British.'

'My government claim—'

'You haven't got a government, Colonel,' Pugh pointed out gently. 'What *was* your government has gone into exile. And I'm sure they aren't interested in the works of a painter who was not, anyway, one of the first division.'

'There are still governmental departments which are functioning,' Da Sangalla pointed out briskly. 'Mine – the Ministry of Monuments and Fine Arts – is one of them. And if Boccaccio Detto Banti did not belong in the first division, why is the British Government so concerned with his work?'

It was a good question and something that had puzzled Pugh, but he didn't show his doubt.

'My government,' he lied, 'has always been a great patron of the arts. You must have heard of the Royal Academy, the Tate. I know you have, in fact, because I know you've visited their exhibitions.'

Da Sangalla was silent for a while as he laid down his cap and gloves, then he straightened up. 'Let us not talk,' he snapped. 'I'm a colonel and you're only a sergeant.'

'Backed by a colonel,' Pugh said briskly.

'Tasker?'

So there *was* something going on. Da Sangalla had obviously arrived hoping to be in front.

'And Baracca,' Pugh said. 'My two to your one, Colonel. Moreover, my two are *conquering* colonels, belonging to the Allied Military Government. Your one has no real portfolio to act because he hasn't got a government to instruct him.'

Da Sangalla obviously decided it was time to stop fencing. 'Where are the paintings, Sergeant?'

'I can't say,' Pugh said.

Da Sangalla's eyes flashed. 'Why not?'

'Because,' Pugh lied, 'I haven't yet found them.'

'I shall search with you.'

'Try it, Colonel, and I'll have a squad of soldiers in here in two minutes to stop you.'

'I demand to see them!'

'In good time, Colonel. And in Naples. At the moment I don't even know how many there are or even if there are any at all.'

'Didn't the brother tell you?'

'The brother is being very cagey.' It was becoming very easy to lie. 'In addition, my instructions are to transport them – when I find them – safely and undisturbed to Naples for examination by experts.'

'I'm an expert. I have always been an expert.'

Pugh smiled. 'But not an *Allied* expert.'

Da Sangalla frowned. 'According to the terms of the armistice between Marshal Badoglio and General Eisenhower,' he said, 'Italy is deemed now to be an ally.'

Pugh smiled. 'I heard the broadcast, Colonello. It said that the Italian Government, recognising the impossibility of continuing the unequal struggle against overwhelmingly superior forces and in order to avoid further grave calamities to the nation, had requested an armistice and that the request had been granted, and as a result, all hostilities between the Italian and the Anglo-American forces would cease forthwith and the Italian forces would resist attacks from any other quarter. Most people assumed that to mean Germans.'

'The Italian people have shown their willingness to resist German aggression.'

'They've still to purge themselves, Colonel. In fact, Italy was left in a worse mess by that so-called government of yours before it fled than it had been before. I might also remind you that, after being imprisoned, the Duce was rescued by the Germans from the Gran Sasso and now heads what *he* and the Germans claim to be the Italian government in the north.'

'Mussolini is a spent force.'

'So is Italy.' Pugh's voice grew stiff with dislike. 'You have no rights to the paintings, Colonel,' he pointed out. 'And I can, if I wish, bring charges against you of attempting to disrupt my efforts to do my duty.'

'Colonel Tasker would make a meal of that.'

'I'm sure he would. And it's as well to remember it. He could remove you from the your position in the Department of Monuments and Fine Arts at any time he wished.'

'I have friends.'

Pugh smiled. 'So, I suspect, has Colonel Tasker. And Colonel Tasker's friends, I imagine, have more power in their elbow than yours.'

Da Sangalla chewed his lip for a while, trying to make up his mind what to argue next. In the end he gave up.

'How many paintings do you think there are?' he asked.

'That will be made known all in good time, Colonel.'

'Surely you can tell me, Sergeant?'

'My report will go first to Colonel Tasker and he will no doubt make known as much of it as he decides fit.'

'Colonel Tasker is a—' Da Sangalla frowned and became silent.

Pugh knew what he had been about to say and privately he agreed with him. But, he suspected, so was Da Sangalla. So was Baracca. Probably so was De

Castro, the art dealer. Probably so was Marco Detto Banti. Of the lot who were involved, the only ones he trusted were Tassinari and Tamara Detto Banti. Tassinari, he felt confident, was so honest it hurt; and he had certainly acquired little comfort for his old age from his work on behalf of his clients. And Tamara Detto Banti surely couldn't be involved in anything underhand when she had tried so hard to give away what to most Italians was a small fortune.

Seeing he was getting nowhere, Da Sangalla left to seek a room at the hotel further up the hill.

Marco was furious. 'Why did you send him away?' he demanded. 'He would have taken the pictures without a murmur. He'd have paid on the spot.'

'What with?' Pugh asked. 'His department has no money.'

'Governments always have money.'

'Not the Italian Government.'

'Perhaps he would have taken them for himself.'

'That's what I'm afraid of. And not paid for them.'

During the afternoon the telephone went. Marco answered it.

'It's De Castro,' he said. 'He's coming up tomorrow. He wants to see the pictures.'

'Tell him they're on their way to Naples,' Pugh said. 'He can see them there.'

'Do you think you're doing the right thing?' Tamara asked.

'For you, yes.'

'Have no fear, Signorina,' Tassinari said. 'This is what I also would do.'

It had been in Pugh's mind for a long time to make sure that Tasker didn't get his hands on the paintings before he'd had a word with Captain Jones. Jones was honest and he was also related to the officer in command of the Special Investigation Branch of the Military Police who, Pugh knew, was able to go direct to the commanding general. It ought to be possible to bypass Tasker until a signal could be sent to London requesting proof of London's interest.

As he was considering the possibilities, Tamara approached him. 'Are you always as forceful as this, Sergeant?'

'You should see me in my best uniform.'

A curious rapport was springing up between them. He got on easily with her and, because she worked with the British in the hospital in Naples, she was able to speak a form of fractured English that was enchanting. While her efforts to pronounce his name had only progressed from Poo to Piu, his Christian name presented little difficulty.

'I must learn to speak English,' she said. 'You must teach me.'

'Nothing would give me greater pleasure.'

'What is it that you do, Sergeant Tomaso?' she asked. 'Is it that you always investigate the pictures?'

'No.' He tried to explain. 'A lot of the time I'm involved investigating Italian girls who wish to marry British soldiers.'

'There is nothing wrong in that.'

'Except that some of the girls merely want to marry so they can get security.'

'There is also nothing wrong with that. It is very common in Italy. And arranged marriages often work. The girl grows to love her husband if he is a good man.'

'What if he isn't? And some of the girls are prostituting themselves.'

Her face grew sad. 'I understand,' she said quietly. She sighed and drew a deep breath. 'Many of these girls are hungry. They are desperate. Sometimes they have a child and their husband is dead. They do it to obtain food for the child. Sometimes not even for money, just for a tin of meat.'

'I know that.'

'And as soon as they marry and are secure they will stop. I think even they will stop as soon as the British

89

and the Americans produce enough food. All Naples is out of work. All Naples is starving.'

'I know that, too.'

'With bread at 160 lire a kilogram and olive oil at 450 a litre, and wages often at 400 lire a month, I think it is not at all odd that these girls sell themselves.' Her small face grew angry. 'I think it is extraordinary that some of the people in Naples who have a job have the strength even to walk to work, let alone do it when they arrive. I am surprised they are not lying dead of starvation in the street, because some of them are trying to keep a family of four or five on no more money than would keep a dog alive.'

'You have your figures assembled.'

'It is part of my job. I work at the hospital and I talk to many of the patients. Will you investigate me, too, Sergeant Piu?'

'Are you intending to marry a British soldier?'

'It hadn't occurred to me.'

'No new *fidanzato*? No suitors?'

'No.'

'I'm surprised.'

'Why?'

'I think if I'd spotted you before I might have been one.'

She stared at him, solemn-faced for a moment, then her small face cracked in an unexpected grin.

Lunch was a threadbare affair. Once more it was British army bully beef and dark-coloured bread, with a few vegetables from the garden at the back of the house.

'It's a good job there's wine,' Marco said gloomily. 'When do we leave?'

'I'll find the town major this afternoon,' Pugh said. 'And commandeer a lorry.'

The rain had changed from the previous day's downpour to a steady drizzle, and there was a raw cold in the air that permeated the house and sent shivers down the spine. Outside, there were one or two new lorries in the square but for some reason the crews looked uncertain. Pugh had talked to the military police that morning and found them all on edge and unwilling to commit one of their vehicles because of rumours that the Germans were building up their strength to the north, and looked as though they were intending to try to cut the main road through Vicinamontane from Naples to Rome.

Ciasca's old hearse approached slowly down the hill on its way back from the cemetery. They had seen it go up the hill not long before, complete with a coffin covered with flowers that looked remarkably like the flowers that had covered Bocco Detto Banti the day before. It was followed by three grim-faced men, all wearing hammer and sickle badges prominently displayed.

'Silvio Minotti,' Marco said. 'He would have led the trade unions here if Mussolini had allowed trade unions. It was consumption.'

Ciasca was on his own, a thin figure in a battered crêpe-draped top hat, his blue fingers holding the reins and trying to urge the old horse on, his ancient frock coat greener than ever in the grey rain-misty light. He had dispensed with attendants, obviously relying on the three grim-faced men and the group of silent relatives in an assortment of shabby black clothes borrowed from neighbours for the occasion. Now the hearse was returning, the mourners dispersed to take wine at the home of the dead man, and Ciasca, his job finished, was smoking a cigarette, doubtless made from butts picked up in the gutter.

They were watching him from the window as Enrichetta appeared in the square. She seemed to be engrossed in her business and Pugh wondered what belongings of Bocco Detto Banti she was intending to sell, because she was carrying a shopping bag made of American cloth. As she passed they heard a faint high whistle in the sky that grew louder and louder. Enrichetta's head lifted, then her eyes widened and she suddenly dropped the shopping bag and bolted. As the bag rolled across the ground a dozen silver knives and forks shot out. Pugh had guessed right about what she was up to and Marco had been correct about her stealing the silver.

The whistle was still increasing, and as it grew louder Tamara looked at Pugh in alarm.

'*Porco Dio!*' Foscari yelled. 'The Germans are shelling us!'

Grabbing Tamara, Pugh threw her to the floor and dropped on top of her. Foscari pushed Avvocato Tassarini in a tottering run up against the wall. Marco threw himself under the table. They were hardly in position when there was a crash outside and the windows fell in and the ceiling came down.

When they lifted their heads, through the whirling dust they saw a house opposite collapsing as though in slow motion into a heap of floors that lay one on top of another like a *mille-feuille* cake. People started to run, and they saw Ciasca's horse break into a canter. The army lorries were already circling the square, heading for the road south. Almost immediately there was another shriek and a crash that shook the house and set the battered chandeliers clinking.

More shells fell. They were coming thick and fast now and Pugh could feel Tamara Detto Banti shuddering beneath him. Outside, one of the trees fell slowly to block the road, then another flash and a crash removed one of the pillars that held up the porch over the front door so that it became lopsided. With the pillar went what' was left of the windows.

A second salvo of shells hit the Palazzo Municipale. It had been evacuated seconds before, everybody running bent double for the air raid shelters, and it seemed almost as if the shells went through the windows and exploded inside. Pugh happened to raise his head just as they went off and he saw the walls bulge, then the lot came down like the collapsed brick-house built by a child. A vast cloud of dust, plaster and pulverised stone, deadened by the drizzle, lifted to the sky.

Ciasca, the undertaker, had fallen off his seat, and the horse was careering in a wild gallop down the hill with him after it. Then another salvo of shells fell and, deciding discretion was the better part of valour, Ciasca changed direction, losing his hat as he did so, and began to head for the open fields. By this time men in khaki were appearing from all directions, and cars and lorries appeared from the north and started to head south. Half a dozen of them came tearing through the village at full speed, rolling and swaying on their springs, the drivers hunched over the wheels, their eyes wild.

Then, abruptly, as if cut off with a knife, the shelling stopped. The silence seemed thick and impenetrable. Pugh lifted his head slowly. Tamara sat up with him. Her face was grey and her hair was covered with plaster dust. Tassinari was still standing bolt upright against the wall as though frozen. He was untouched but the clouds of plaster from the fallen ceiling had coated him so that he looked like a ghost.

As Pugh rose to his feet, he caught a glimpse of more cars hurtling through the village. One of them he recognised at once as Colonel Da Sangalla's. The Colonel was minus his hat and clearly had no intention of staying. A second car drew up across the square and the Mayor, Sansovino, with his henchmen, appeared from one of the streets behind the ruins of the town hall. As they hurried to the car, another shell landed in the square and they all flung themselves flat. The smoke drifted away, their heads lifted and there was a great deal of arm-waving, then, tyres screaming, the car started with a jerk and set off in a wide circle round the piazza and towards the road to the south. As it vanished, Pugh drew a deep breath. If nothing else, Sansovino's departure meant that he could relax for a while and wouldn't need to be constantly looking over his shoulder to make sure that the Detto Bantis were safe.

The hearse had finally come to a stop. The panic-stricken horse had crashed through the hedge into the garden of the Ca' di Leone, where a branch catching under one of the weeping chrome angels jammed the hearse. Since it could move no further, the horse clearly considered there was no point in worrying any more, and its head was down, munching on the grass. Of the owner the only sign was his top hat lying in the road.

Just as everyone in the little town turned out to study the damage, the bombardment started again. It was an old trick of the Germans to catch soldiers making repairs, and everybody disappeared again like leaves before a high wind. On and off for the rest of the afternoon the shells continued to fall in salvoes and all the time they could hear the thudding of guns to the north.

'*Vicinamontane sarà destrutta!*' Tamara gasped. 'They'll destroy the town.'

Eventually lorries began to crash and rattle past, carrying khaki-clad men or dragging bouncing guns.

'They're pulling out, Signor Sergente,' Foscari said. 'I think it is time for us to go, too.'

They ran to the front of the house but, as they appeared in the street to find out what was happening, another salvo of shells drove them indoors again, to lie flat on their faces close to the wall. It was obvious what the Germans were up to. They were trying to cut the road in the hope of trapping the Allied troops.

When the shells finally stopped, they went out into the street again. There was no sign of the army, just a stream of civilians in carts, on mules and on foot, heading south.

'What about the pictures?' Tassinari asked.

'We'd better hide them,' Pugh said. 'There's enough rubbish in the cellars to cover a house.'

Without argument, without question, they headed in

a body for the cellar, where the paintings were still waiting, crated up ready to leave for Naples. At one side of the cellar was a pantry and beyond it a cold room. Enrichetta's huge kitchen cupboard stood alongside the door.

'In there,' Pugh said.

Between them, they carried the paintings into the cold room, then they dragged the huge cupboard into place across the door so that it was completely hidden. Staring at it, they decided there was no sign of anything beyond the pantry.

'They're all right there for a while,' Pugh said. 'We'll come back for them when the Germans have gone.'

As they dusted their hands, Marco indicated the back of the house. 'I think one dropped round there somewhere,' he said. 'I'd better go and see what happened.'

Those inhabitants of the town who hadn't already left seemed to be standing in the battered piazza staring at the ruins of their town hall. It had been a square, ugly building with a flattish roof minus a lot of tiles, its walls chipped and broken, whole areas where the plaster had fallen away showing the bricks underneath like patches of disease. There were notices on the wall dating back to the days of the Fascists, but the fasces and other insignia had all been removed with the busts and portraits on the downfall of Mussolini. The stones had also been layered with black-edged notices giving the names of the newly-dead, and under the old notices of *Evviva Mussolini* new ones of *Abasso Mussolini* had been added. It hadn't been a very impressive edifice but it had been the town hall and now there was nothing, and what was left of the population was standing mourning it.

As Pugh turned away, he realised that Ciasca's hearse was still in the orchard of the Ca' di Leone with the horse, so they disentangled it from the tree, put Ciasca's top hat inside and unharnessed the horse. It had clearly decided that it was on to a good thing, with far better eating than in its normal pasturage, and showed no inclination to move. They were still discussing what to do with it when Marco returned.

'They hit your car,' he said cheerfully.

The shell seemed to have landed inside the vehicle, and the garage, made out of the stables, was pock-marked with splinters, while the door hung off its hinges in slivers of wood. Where the Fiat had stood was a small crater, still smoking, and the car lay scattered across the courtyard and orchard in a hundred and one pieces. A wheel rested against a tree, a wing reposed among the branches, a tyre, flickering with flame, lay in the grass.

Pugh stared at it blankly.

'It could be put together,' Foscari said cheerfully.

'How long would it take?'

'A year or two perhaps.'

Pugh looked about him. 'I think we ought to be on our way,' he said. 'Those shells didn't fall on Vicinamontane for nothing. The Germans will be here soon, I reckon.'

He wasn't far wrong.

8

The first indication that the Germans were coming was the noise of engines and, turning to gaze up the hill, Pugh was the first to realise what was happening. For a moment, he stared, then he looked down at himself and remembered he was wearing a British uniform.

'Holy Jesus Christ!' he said and bolted for the house.

Tamara was just behind him. 'What is it, Piu? It is only the Germans. They have been before and they will soon go.'

He gestured at his uniform. 'In this, I'm heading straight for a prison camp.'

'*Mamma mia!*' She caught on at once and shouted for the others to come inside.

'*La giacchetta!*' she snapped at Marco, and almost dragged the old dinner jacket from his back. 'Find clothes!'

'There aren't any clothes!'

'There must be!'

As everybody scuttled off, the Germans began to fill the square. First of all it was a lorry carrying infantrymen armed to the teeth with automatic weapons and grenades, hard-faced men whose eyes were shadowed by steel helmets, their bodies laden with equipment. As the lorry pulled to a stop, other vehicles arrived and men hurried off to set up strongpoints in the places where they had been established during the previous occupation. A car halted with a squeal of brakes, and officers began to climb out, hung about with map cases, binoculars and weapons.

Foscari took one look at them and, a true opera lover,

97

fell back on *Pagliacci.* '*La commedia,*' he wailed, '*è finita!*'

Inside the house everyone was turning out clothes. A checked shirt smeared with paint was discovered among the rubbish in the studio; an old scarf was contributed by Avvocato Tassinari; then Marco came down with an armful of worn and faded garments.

'Bocco's,' he said.

Within minutes Pugh and Foscari looked like Italian civilians, and Tamara had stuffed their uniforms into the wood-burning stove in the kitchen. They were still admiring themselves when the door rattled to heavy knocking.

Tamara opened it. She showed no sign of nervousness and even acted with considerable aplomb. On the step outside was a German officer. He was clearly not a fighting soldier because he wore thick spectacles and his weaponry consisted only of a notebook and a pen.

'Klemper,' he announced. 'Hauptmann Hermann Klemper, Sonderauftrag Linz.'

They looked at him blankly and he explained.

'Sonderauftrag Linz is the special mission set up to appreciate and safeguard works of art. The Führer was born at Linz and it is his ambition to make it the artistic Mecca of the new Europe.'

Tassinari's eyebrows lifted. 'The new Europe?' he said. 'I think, Signor Capitano, that by the time he has finished there will not be much Europe left at all.' He smiled. 'And perhaps even the Führer will not be around to administer it.'

Klemper frowned because even to him it was becoming obvious that what Tassinari said was true. 'No matter,' he said. 'The fact that things are happening in Russia of which we do not speak is of no importance. I have my instructions and I must obey them. Naturally, the Führer's vision has to be placed in cold storage until the war is over, but there is no reason why the preparations should not proceed methodically.'

Tassinari's mouth twisted in a small smile. Pugh knew

what he was thinking. It was typical of the Germans to create even their dreams in painstaking fashion.

Klemper was standing with his hands behind his back now, studying his surroundings.

'I need accommodation for myself and my party,' he said, 'and this house seems to be one of the few undamaged with enough rooms. I have a report here from the Colonel of the 179th Regiment, who was billeted in the town recently. We will board up the windows. You have three floors, each with several large rooms, together with a set of basement rooms used by the staff.'

'The staff,' Marco said bitterly, 'was one old woman who has since left.'

'Never mind. Who is the owner?'

Avvocato Tassinari happened to be standing at the front of the group facing him and, as Tamara opened her mouth to answer, he stepped forward and spoke with an alacrity and alertness that startled Pugh.

'I am Tassinari, Filippo,' he said. 'The house belonged to the painter, Boccaccio Detto Banti. I am his cousin. I think perhaps it now belongs to me.'

Standing in the background, feeling that he stood out like a sore thumb – a *British* sore thumb at that – Pugh held his breath.

The German was smiling. 'Boccaccio Detto Banti, eh?' he said. 'That is very convenient and of great interest to me.' He gestured. 'Who are these people?'

Tassinari indicated Marco. 'My cousin, Marcopolo Detto Banti. He came with me.'

'How did he get here? Is there a car?'

'There was. Your shells have just destroyed it.'

Klemper frowned. 'A pity. Vehicles are at a premium these days. And these others?'

Tassinari bowed. 'Cousins also.' He gestured at Foscari, who was standing rigid with horror at the thought of being taken off and shot for not reporting to the Germans as he'd been ordered. 'Foscari, Enzio. He is not very bright. He says little.' Tassinari touched his head, and turned to Pugh. 'Another cousin, Cavalcassella, Ettore.'

Klemper smiled at Tamara, who stared back at him hostilely.

'His wife?'

Tamara's startled eyes met Pugh's. Pugh nodded, moved closer and put his arm round her shoulders. She gave a little twitch as though to shake it off, then changed her mind and put her arm round his waist.

'How did *they* get here? The car?'

'They came by bus. A very old bus. It was very tiring.'

Pugh's mind was working fast but Tassinari was doing very well, because Hauptmann Klemper seemed to be accepting without question everything he said.

'Why are they all here?'

'My cousin is dead,' Tassinari explained. 'He was buried yesterday. They came for the funeral. Also I think,' he added, 'to see what they might pick up in the form of legacies. This is a very Italian habit. But I think they will be disappointed. There is no money. There is no money anywhere in Italy.'

'I see.' Klemper nodded. 'We shall require the main part of the house. You will be allowed to use the hall and the basement rooms.'

'And my cousin's studio?'

Klemper's head jerked round. 'That will be out of bounds to everyone,' he rapped. 'There must be paintings in there of great value. They need to be assessed by experts.'

Tassinari's frail frame moved in a gigantic shrug. 'Alas, Signor Capitano, I regret there is nothing. We have already looked, of course.'

Klemper frowned. 'There *must* be paintings. Boccaccio Detto Banti was a prolific painter.'

'Not in his old age, Signor Capitano. He painted nothing for years and, like most Italians, he had to sell off what he possessed to raise money to buy food.'

Klemper clearly didn't believe him and Pugh wondered if he had inside knowledge of what the house contained.

'There must be sketches,' he said. 'There must be something.'

Tassinari shrugged again. 'I understood,' he said, 'that everything was deposited in the Palazzo Municipale, the town hall.'

'Where is the town hall?'

Tassinari gave another of his huge shrugs, opened the door and pointed. 'There, Signor Capitano. Across the square. You have just destroyed it. *Che desolazione!*'

Klemper strode to the door and stared over the assembled vehicles, before turning to the young lieutenant who accompanied him. 'Hoggeimer, we shall need bulldozers.' He swung back to Tassinari. 'Where would they have been placed?'

'In the cellars, I imagine, Signor Capitano.'

'Who would know?'

'The *sindaco*, Signor Capitano. These are men who have been put in charge by the Anglo-Americans, to take the place of the Fascist *podestas*. I think many of them are gangsters ruled by the reigning gangsters in Naples.'

'What's his name?'

'Sansovino, Vicenzo.'

'Where is he now?'

'I saw him bolting south as the shells started falling.'

'Himmelherrgott!' Klemper turned to Hoggeimer. 'Find someone who was employed across there! Anyone! I must know what happened to the paintings.'

'It will be difficult for the Signore Capitano,' Tassinari said gently. 'As I have said, the *sindaco* was a crook. Most of the *sindacos* are crooks. He was not the sort of man who would be likely to tell his staff what he was going to do with anything valuable. I have no doubt he was expecting a substantial reward. Perhaps he even had plans to keep a painting or two for himself. Perhaps even he had plans to keep *all* the paintings.'

Klemper was looking angry and alarmed at the same time. 'Get on with it, Hoggeimer! Find out!'

Pugh could hardly repress a smile. It was a brilliant piece of improvisation. With the town hall now only a pile of rubble it was going to take Klemper some time to discover that the paintings he was looking for weren't there.

'I understood there *were* paintings,' Klemper said. 'I *heard* there were paintings.'

'Who from, Signore?' Tassinari's manner was polite but his eyes glinted suddenly.

Klemper took a turn up and down the room before swinging round to face Tassinari. 'Word was passed to us. It was reported from the Kunstschutz, the official organisation safeguarding art treasures, that there *were* pictures. They should have been investigated when our troops were here before, but the Sonderauftrag Linz was busy in the north. There are many treasures in Florence which have to be assessed and safeguarded. We had better hurry.'

'There is no hurry, Signore, surely.'

'Isn't there?' Klemper eyed Tassinari doubtfully. 'I think there is, because there will not be another summer after this. In the meantime,' he went on, 'we have other things to occupy our time. The Church of San Isidro at Avizano has an altarpiece by Simonetta, and it will need to be removed to a safe place where it can't be damaged. That will keep us busy until Hoggeimer has learned the whereabouts of the Detto Bantis. For the moment we will look at the accommodation.'

They led him into the basement. The cold room where the paintings were hidden was obscured by the cupboard they had dragged into place and Klemper didn't investigate further.

'Three rooms,' he said. 'A kitchen, a bedroom and a store room.' He studied the room where old Enrichetta had slept and the big double bed where she had spread her ample body, then peered next door into the store room, which now, with its stores long gone, was empty apart from a single iron bedstead. 'There is room here for three of you,' he pointed out. He gestured at Tassinari. 'You can have the bed, old man. The other two will sleep on the floor.'

'Why are we not to be allowed home?'

'Where are your homes?'

'Naples.'

Klemper smiled. 'You are now in the German zone. It will be difficult.' He looked at Pugh. 'Signor Cavalcassella and his wife can have the double bed,' he said. 'No one can say that we are not trying to be helpful.'

Tamara was staring horrified at Pugh as Klemper continued. 'We shall need meals, of course. You will be given rations. Our orderlies will serve the food but you will cook for us. I expect you can do that. I expect also that you will help yourself to what's left, but I suppose we mustn't complain. It's something we've learned to expect from Italians.'

By late afternoon, a bulldozer was scrabbling about in the ruins of the town hall, Klemper had set up an office in the big salon off the hall and men were examining the Church of San Isidro in Avizano with a view to removing the altarpiece. Among the workmen they had recruited and driven there by lorry were several from Vicinamontane, among them Pugh and Foscari. When they arrived, they found Della Croce, the student-butcher boy, also there, his job a clandestine one to find out exactly where it was intended to take the altarpiece.

'We Italians,' he told Pugh quietly, 'have shown little heart for becoming cannon-fodder in a futile war, but there is no lack of courage in our attempts to retain our national treasures. There is more sense in fighting for a Titian or a Tintoretto than for a stretch of dusty ground in North Africa. We shall have difficulty after it is all over, of course, claiming *everything* back, because we are ex-enemies and there will be too many vultures among the Anglo-Americans. But we shall manage it, because there are also a few honest men.' He pointed at the altarpiece. 'They might not even get very far with it, because I've been informed that partisans are gathering.'

Lieutenant Hoggeimer had been able to find out nothing about Sansovino, beyond that by this time he was well on his way to Naples and that if he had placed the Detto Bantis in the vaults of the town hall he had taken great care not to inform anyone.

'He was a crook, Herr Kapitän,' he informed Klemper. 'Thanks to the gullibility of the Anglo-Americans, he got himself appointed here and was living on the place like a bloodsucker.'

'We Germans do things more thoroughly,' Klemper said placidly. 'I don't think *we* would have appointed him.'

Hoggeimer smiled. 'There would be no point,' he said. 'We have gauleiters.'

Klemper frowned but Hoggeimer showed no sign of perturbation. He was a clever young man who had been an art student until his call-up, and he had long since decided that while he was safeguarding treasures for Hitler he might also safeguard a few things for himself because it was clear that, despite what the Führer said, the war was going to be lost and it would be difficult when peace came.

As the truck deposited the Italians back in Vicina-montane, Pugh noticed the student-butcher boy deep in conversation with Marco Detto Banti. As he left, Pugh drew Marco to one side. 'What does he want?' he demanded.

'Money,' Marco said. 'I said we haven't got any.'

'Why you?'

'He thinks the place is full of paintings which can be sold to the Germans. He said he should sell them and use the money to buy guns for the partisans.'

'Does he know about the paintings in the cellar?'

'Not a thing. He's guessing.'

Sitting round the remains of a meal at the table in the basement kitchen, all of them wearing coats against the chill in the cellars, Pugh faced the others. They had eaten well. German rations weren't as good as American rations, but they were more substantial than the rations the Italians had had to endure.

The Germans had not worried them and Klemper had even gone out of his way to be polite, but the place had changed. Instead of the free and easy air of a family house, even a family house divided by disagreement, it had become stiff and formal. With the cigars the Germans smoked, it had even acquired a different smell.

He looked at Foscari. While it wasn't important for Tamara and the other two, it was certainly important that he and Foscari disappeared before the Germans discovered who they were. Failure would mean a prison camp for Pugh and probably death for Foscari. Foscari was well aware of what the consequences might be and, since the arrival of the Germans, he had hardly left Pugh's side, as if he regarded him as some sort of lucky charm that would save him.

'It's time we left,' Pugh said. 'How do we get away?'

Tassinari smiled. 'There's only one sure way of getting *anything* in Italy,' he said. 'Bribery. Perhaps we could use one of Bocco's paintings to get us out of the town.'

'We've still got to get through the German lines.'

Tassinari smiled. '*Allora*, let us take two then.'

'Why not take the lot?' Tamara said. 'We might save some of them.'

'We'd need a lorry for that.'

'There aren't any lorries.'

'Then we must find a car.'

'You can't get them in a car. They're too big. You'd have to take them out of the frames.'

'Then why *not* take them out of the frames?'

They stared at each other. Now that the idea of taking

the paintings with them had been put forward everybody seemed to be accepting it without question.

'In that case,' Pugh said, 'we'd better start straight away.'

'It'll take most of the night, sir,' Foscari pointed out.

'And we can't leave tomorrow in daylight,' Marco said. 'It would have to be during tomorrow night. They'll not have dug down to the vaults under the town hall by then.'

'Where are we going to find transport? We can't walk to Naples.'

That floored them. There weren't any cars. Everybody knew that. There were only old vehicles pulled by skeletal horses – carts, carriages and—

'Hearses,' Pugh said, sitting bolt upright.

They all stared at him. 'We've *got* transport,' he said. 'In the garden. Even the horse to pull it.'

'The hearse?'

'Why not? We've just had one funeral. Let's have another!'

'Whose? The Germans will want to know.'

'Enrichetta's. She's disappeared. Who's to know she didn't die. We drive away with the hearse containing a coffin, but what's inside the coffin won't be the remains of Enrichetta. The paintings will be inside.'

Tassinari nodded gravely. 'Funerals are always good. Italians love death. They never put aside their black because families are large and there's always someone they can mourn.'

'Where do we get a coffin?'

'I can make one, sir,' Foscari said.

'What from?'

Foscari indicated Enrichetta's big kitchen cupboard. 'Pine,' he said. 'Cheap. Soft wood. Let us take it to pieces.'

'Can you?'

'We have tools, sir. A hammer. Nails. Screws. A saw.'

'It's not coffin wood.'

'Nobody in Italy will argue, sir. These days coffins are made of all kinds of wood.'

Pugh grinned. 'Make it big, Enzio,' he said. 'Enrichetta was a fat woman.'

They were all involved. Marco disappeared outside, found the horse – still miraculously unstolen – and locked it in what was left of the stables. It was already looking considerably better for the grazing in the orchard and even seemed to resent the move. Nobody had claimed the hearse, so they moved that into the carriage house.

'Go and find Ciasca, Marco,' Pugh said. 'Offer him money. Hire his hearse. Anything you like.'

'We'll need flowers,' Tamara said. 'You can't have a funeral without flowers.'

'Go and find some.'

Marco came back half an hour later with the information that Ciasca had disappeared into the hills. 'His neighbours said he didn't like handling bodies,' he announced. 'He inherited the business when his brother died six months ago. But he was superstitious and never liked it. The hearse and the horse are ours.'

Soon afterwards, Tamara returned with her arms full of blooms. She looked pink-faced and ashamed.

'I took them off the grave of the man they buried this morning,' she said. 'I think they came originally from my father's. If I hadn't taken them I suppose someone else would have.'

Taking the cupboard to pieces was a problem, especially as they had to be as quiet as possible. But Foscari knew how cupboards were put together and they were able to do it with a minimum of noise. Old Tassinari acted as carpenter's mate. They worked hard, absorbed in the task, until Foscari forgot where he was.

'For Christ's sake,' Pugh said. 'This is no bloody time to start singing!'

'*Mi scusi.*' Foscari looked abashed. 'I forget. It is

Rodolfo singing to the very cold Mimi. It is very Italian to sing opera. In Italy we are in constant intimacy with death, and this is why consumptive heroines like Violetta and Mimi are so real to us.'

Most of the nails came out of the crates from the back of the cellar, laboriously straightened by Pugh or Tamara, and the screws came from old Enrichetta's cupboard. In the bottom of the cupboard were deep wide drawers with brass handles, which Foscari removed to decorate the coffin. They were only held on by screws and would never have been enough to lift a body, so he drilled holes and attached ropes that lay inside the handles so that the lifting could be done with those. Nobody in Italy would ever query it. Since the war people had been laid to rest in far worse coffins than the one Foscari had made.

'We'll have to weight it, sir,' he said realistically. 'If anybody sees us lifting it, it must look as though it's got something inside it.'

They found several large stones outside which they supplemented with heavy kitchen equipment.

'We've also got to pad it, sir,' Foscari pointed out. 'If the stones slide about, it will sound a hard and bony body, I think.'

Searching among the rubbish in the cellar, in a big oak trunk they found a set of blue velvet curtains with gold fringes, together with the gold-tasselled ropes which had held their folds in place. By a miracle, neither the mice nor the moths had been at them and, though the colours had faded a little on the edges, they were in excellent condition.

'They came from the studio,' Marco explained. 'It was originally a bedroom.'

As they lifted them out, a small treasure trove fell to the floor – brooches, miniatures, bracelets, and three small oil paintings about thirty-six centimetres square.

'As we thought,' Pugh said. 'Enrichetta *was* helping herself.'

108

As Marco reached for one of the oils, Pugh pushed his hand away.

'Leave it,' he rapped. He glanced at Tamara and, picking up the painting, stood for a moment, staring at it. Taking it across to the light, he examined it more closely. 'Whatever the others might be,' he said slowly, 'this is Bocco Detto Banti at his best. This is the first division period, before he grew old and got arthritis and started drinking too much. This is a first division painting.'

Tamara appeared alongside him. 'Are you sure?'

'I'm certain. *These* are valuable, twice as valuable as the others, in fact. And these are a size we can get away easily without removing the frames. Whatever we do with the others, we've got to well and truly hide these.'

There was plenty of straw among the crates, which they used to pad the stones. When Foscari had finished, they laid the canvasses in the coffin and were about to put the lid on when Tassinari stopped them.

'We must keep one out,' he said. 'For the bribe. For the one thing that can always get you favours in Italy.'

They argued around the subject for a while but they all knew that Tassinari was right.

'We have nothing else,' Tassinari explained. 'And fourteen paintings and freedom are better than fifteen paintings and no freedom. A Detto Banti – even a poor one – is a splendid ransom.'

They studied the pictures for a while, trying to choose what they considered the least valuable.

'This one,' Tassinari suggested. 'What he calls *A Farmer Selling a Cow.*'

It was an uninspired painting, with two bored-looking men standing alongside an even more bored-looking cow.

'Not one of his best,' Tassinari admitted. 'A poor painting from a poor period. He stared at the three new ones they had found with a warm expression. 'Not like those. But, of course, nobody need know that but us.'

*

It was almost morning when they finally sat back. Loaded with stones and packed with the paintings in straw secured by one of the velvet curtains, the coffin stood in the cellar. All they had to do was wait through the day and leave after dark the next night. It meant sneaking the coffin out to the stables, but they felt they could do it, and that no one would stop a hearse. With air raids, funerals in Italy were being held at strange times, especially near the front, where shelling might be expected. People buried their dead late at night or in the early morning, to avoid being spotted from some look-out post in the hills and receiving a few explosives to speed the corpse on its way. As they finished, Marco produced a bottle of brandy from the back of the cellar.

'The last of Bocco's stock,' he said.

There was a shortage of glasses but they made do with cups and toasted the success of the venture. By this time, old Tassinari was almost out on his feet.

'I think it's time we got some sleep,' Pugh said. 'We're going to be up most of tomorrow night.'

As the other three headed for the comfortless store room, Tamara was in a cheerful mood, delighted that they had found a means of cheating the Germans of their loot.

'It isn't that the paintings mean much to me, Piu,' she said happily. 'I didn't have much and it wouldn't matter if I went on not having much. But I don't like to see that monster in Germany taking what belongs to Italy.'

As she closed the door and took off her coat, she suddenly realised she was alone in the room with Pugh and a large double bed. It didn't seem to be a very comfortable-looking bed, and old Enrichetta had clearly not been very fussy because they had found a mouse's nest in a pair of old shoes in the cupboard; but Tamara stared in alarm first at the bed, then at Pugh, then she turned back to the door.

'I can't stay here, Piu,' she said quickly. 'They think I'm your wife. They expect me to sleep in your bed.'

She stood gazing at him over the coat she clutched to her chest. There was no sound from the floor above and only a subdued muttering from the room next door.

'Take it easy,' Pugh said gently, doing his best to avoid touching her and setting off a show of hysterics.

'I am all right!' She held up her hand to indicate she was calm but her voice was unsteady and a little higher than normal. 'I'm not afraid. I have been fighting off men half my life. But' – she repeated the words flatly and firmly – 'I cannot sleep in here with you, Sergeant Piu. Not even if the Germans think I should.'

As she moved towards the door, Pugh stepped forward and put his hand on it. They were face to face, close enough for their shoulders to be brushing.

'Steady on,' he said gently. 'Even if you can't sleep in here with me, you can hardly sleep next door with the other three, and you certainly can't sleep upstairs with the Germans.'

She slowly released the door handle and stood back, suddenly close to breakdown.

'And if you leave,' he went on, 'they'll ask questions. Then what will you tell them? My name and your name? That you're Tamara Detto Banti and I'm Tom Pugh, of British Field Security, stationed in Naples and about to disappear into the blue with a number of valuable articles which they are at this moment seeking in the ruins of the Palazzo Municipale. If they knew you were Bocco Detto Banti's daughter, they'd question you. And they have means of making you tell.'

Her eyes were on his face. 'What would happen if they found out?'

'I would be whipped into a prisoner of war camp and they'd probably shoot Foscari, old Tassinari, Marco – and probably even you – for harbouring a British soldier.'

Suddenly the strain they'd been under all day seemed to break inside her and she was wilting quietly from weariness. Before he knew what was happening, she was sobbing with a terrible desperation, chewing at her knuckles to keep the sound from coming out.

Pugh put his hands on her shoulders, and she let her hands drop to her sides and leaned against him, her distrust forgotten. She was glad he was there, simply glad and grateful. He put his hands gently on her cheeks and lifted her face and held her like that until the shuddering went out of her.

'That's it. Let it go. You'll feel better afterwards.'

'*Mai*! Never!' She straightened up abruptly, his words a challenge as he intended them to be. As she lifted her head, dry-eyed now, he cuffed her softly on the jaw.

'I'm not going to cry, Piu,' she said. 'I haven't cried since I was a child.'

She pushed him away angrily, but behind her sharpness was a feeling of gratitude. 'Very well,' she said. 'It doesn't matter. I'll sleep on the floor.'

'It'll be damned uncomfortable' Pugh said. 'I'm sleeping on the bed. Fully clothed,' he added. 'You could have half.'

'I'll sleep on the floor.'

He shrugged and, dragging the mattress to the floor for her, handed her the blanket and stretched out on the bare springs of the bed.

She sat on the mattress and studied him. 'You will be very cold, I think, Piu.'

'I'll manage.'

She lay down and tried to sleep but she was overtired and worried, and her nerves were stretched taut. Then she became aware of Pugh tossing uncomfortably on the bed.

'Sergeant Piu,' she said softly. 'Can you not sleep?'

'No,' he growled.

'Why not?'

'It's cold.'

She sat up, pleased to be able to talk. 'You must have the blanket.'

'If I have it, *you'll* be cold.'

There was a long silence. 'You are still wearing your clothes?'

'I'd be cold without them.'

'I also am cold. You had better come and share the blanket with me.'

'Much better to put the mattress on the bed and share it there. It's softer.'

There was a long silence then she stood up. 'I think you are right, Piu,' she said.

Tamara woke slowly and unwillingly. As consciousness flooded over her she saw the low stone ceiling and the white-washed walls and for a moment thought she was in a tomb. Until reality came to her with a violent jerk, she lay tense and rigid, her breath held, terrified. Then, as she realised where she was, she felt for Pugh, whose back against hers had helped to dispel the chilliness of the basement room.

His reassuring presence was not there. There was no sign of him, and she was suddenly scared. But, as she sat up, the door opened and Pugh entered, holding a cracked mug.

'Coffee' he said. 'Good enough, I suspect, to be black market American K rations.

She looked at him gratefully, feeling the need to apologise.

'I am sorry, Piu,' she said. 'I should not have thought the things I thought.'

His expression was blank. 'What things were those?'

She frowned. 'I am not sure now. But they were wrong things.' She grinned suddenly. 'Perhaps you will now have to investigate me with the other girls you are investigating. Have I not slept with a man?' The grin came again. 'Perhaps there is more to it than I thought, in fact. It was certainly warmer than I expected.'

9

The day dragged. The rain had stopped but there were puddles of water everywhere and the streets were muddy. The temperature had dropped, too, so that, with the damp, it was cheerless and chilly.

Whenever two of the people in the basement of the Ca' di Leone came together, they found themselves discussing what was to happen that night.

'Holy Mary, Mother of God,' Marco said, 'I'll be glad when it's over. Wouldn't we be better simply to offer the pictures to the Germans?'

'No,' Tassinari snapped.

'They'd pay.'

'The Germans don't pay,' Pugh said. 'Why should they, when they can just point a gun at you and say "I want"? They've already dismantled the altarpiece at Avizano. Della Croce told me. It's in a crate labelled *Beschlagnahmt* – confiscated – with the initials AH – Adolph Hitler – on it. It's going to the collection he's building up, not for his pleasure but for his own glorification.'

'An irony,' Tassinari said cheerfully, 'when you consider he's started losing the war. It will be recovered.'

'If it arrives,' Pugh pointed out dryly. 'It has to pass through a lot of voracious hands first.'

The bulldozer was still ploughing backwards and forwards in the wreckage of the Palazzo Municipale, but so far it hadn't made much impression and the Germans didn't seem a great deal nearer the vaults underneath. Their success in one of their ventures and their lack of success in the other had kept them out of the hair of the people in the basement of the Ca' di Leone, but they guessed that it wouldn't be for long.

Klemper was a restless man and, with the altarpiece despatched north and the work on the Palazzo Municipale ruins still hampering him in his quest for the Detto Bantis, he had turned his attention to other things. In Crocifisso, further to the west, there was an Adoration of the Lamb, reputed to be by Tintoretto, and he had sent Hoggeimer off to investigate and, if it was genuine, to look into the possibilities of removing it.

'The Führer's orders are clear,' he told Pugh gravely. 'Moveable works of art will be taken from the place where they are at the present, or modified in any way whatsoever, only with the written authority of the military organisation and the district senior officer of the Sonderauftrag.' He smiled. 'I have that authority from the military and I am the district senior officer of the Sonderauftrag.'

They ate well at lunchtime. The meal was cooked by Tamara – assisted by Foscari, who could add cooking to his other skills – and carried to the German orderlies by Pugh, who could hear everything that was being said.

'I think we shall do well out of this in the end,' Klemper was saying. 'The Simonetta altarpiece and the Detto Bantis are valuable. And, if we are lucky, perhaps the Tintoretto *Adoration* from Crocifisso. The Führer will be pleased.'

During the afternoon, Tamara approached Pugh shyly with a request that he should accompany her to Boccaccio Detto Banti's grave.

'He was my father,' she explained. 'I never knew him but I feel I am abandoning him to the Germans. I would like to kneel there and say a little prayer.'

'I'll come,' Pugh said.

'It will not look wrong. After all, you are supposed to be my husband and we shall be paying our last respects.' She managed a smile. 'And perhaps a few bad words, too, because we have told the Germans he left us nothing.'

115

They walked slowly up the hill in cool spring sunshine, Tamara clutching a handful of wild flowers. At Detto Banti's grave, she laid down the flowers and knelt for a moment. As she finished, he took her elbow and helped her to her feet. She gave him a puzzled look.

'You are kinder than you look, Piu,' she murmured.

It was late in the afternoon when they returned, and the bulldozer by the Palazzo Municipale had stopped. But the vaults in the basement were still uncovered, though the altarpiece from Avizano had already disappeared northwards towards Germany.

'I have noted the address,' the student-butcher boy, Della Croce, murmured to Pugh. 'Schloss Thuerntal, near Kremsmuenster. I have looked it up. It is in Austria.'

Hoggeimer had still not returned from Crocifisso but Klemper seemed to be thinking of the possibility of rewards, and the evening meal was a large one with several bottles of wine. One of the young soldiers sang:

Nun müss ich gar
Um dein Aug' und Haar

Eventually the conversation grew noisy, boastful, but with an underlying nervousness that to Pugh indicated that none of the Germans felt sure any longer of winning the war. By midnight the house was silent and, sitting on the bed in the basement room alongside Tamara, Pugh gestured. 'Time we left,' he said.

The others were waiting in the store in a fug of smoke from German cigarettes Marco had cadged. All of them were nervous, Avvocato Tassinari looking so tired he seemed to be a walking corpse, devoid of flesh or even of very much life, his eyes glazed, his skin grey.

They took the ropes of the coffin that Foscari had made and hoisted it up gently.

'Take it easy, Signori,' Foscari warned. 'Don't bang it on anything. It's not as strong as it ought to be and we don't want it to collapse.'

With Pugh and Foscari carrying the front of the

coffin, and Marco and old Tassinari the other end, they struggled up the stairs, breathing heavily and all hissing frantic pleas for silence. They were followed by Tamara, who was slung about with bags and old army sidepacks containing food they had saved from the day's meals and two bottles of the Germans' wine. Sliding the coffin silently over the rollers in the back of the hearse, all newly greased with German butter to stop them squeaking, they began to lead out the old horse to the shafts. The clatter of its hooves staggered them.

'Back,' Pugh said in a harsh whisper that was as near to a shriek as it could be. 'Back in the stables!'

'We'll never get away with it,' he said, pushing the startled animal inside. 'It'll wake Klemper!'

They waited with bated breath for the Germans to pour out of the house and arrest them all, but nothing happened and they could only assume that they had not been disturbed.

'They probably thought it was just old Fiorello here, tramping around in his stall,' Pugh whispered. 'Driving out of the yard would certainly wake them.'

'The hearse has rubber tyres, sir,' Foscari pointed out.

'What a pity the horse hasn't got rubber hooves.'

'The curtains!' Tamara suggested. 'What about the velvet curtains? Can't we use them to muffle its feet? A friend of mine saved their mule when the Germans came, by padding its hooves with sacks and leading it into the hills in the dark.'

The old blue curtains were brought out in a bundle from the cellar and tied round the horse's feet with the gold cords which had once held them draped at the windows of the studio. The horse looked startled at the tassels but not particularly offended.

'I expect,' Tamara whispered, 'it's seen a lot of funny things in its time.'

'Mussolini, for instance,' Pugh suggested.

She laughed, faintly hysterical. 'Vittorio Emmanuelo, the King. He was even funnier than Mussolini.'

She was still clutching the ancient blue velvet of the deep pelmet and she looked guiltily at Pugh. 'Can't I keep this?' she begged. 'It is too good to be walked on by a horse. I could make myself a dress out of it.' She held it up in front of her. 'I think the colour suits me, no?'

'It matches your eyes,' he said, and she blushed and stuffed the pelmet into the hearse.

'I'll drive,' Pugh said. 'Avvocato Tassinari can sit with me. You as well. The other two will have to ride in the back somehow.' He paused. 'It's a strange way to go to a funeral, I suppose.'

'I've seen stranger funerals recently,' Tamara said. 'I doubt if anyone will even look twice.' She picked up the undertaker's top hat and placed it on Pugh's head. 'You can be the uncle from Rome.'

With Marco and Foscari walking behind, Pugh led the old horse out of the yard. The padded hooves and the rubber-tyred wheels made no sound. The night was dark and pricked by stars but there was no moon. To the south they could hear the thudding of artillery and occasionally the faint tap-tapping of a machine gun. The trees stood up starkly against the silver of the sky and they could just see the faint outline of the Matese Mountains in the distance. As soon as they were clear of the house, they removed the curtains from the horse's hooves and began to stuff them into the rear of the hearse with the coffin.

'Folded,' Pugh insisted. 'You don't use a hearse with a coffin in it as a repository for muddy curtains. Put them in so the mud doesn't show and up at the front where they won't be seen.'

They reached the edge of the town without being stopped. Once a soldier with a rifle stepped out of the shadows and Tamara explained, without a tremor in her voice, that they were burying her grandfather in his native village and hoped to be on the way before daylight when aircraft would be over.

'We're going to Massinicorvo because the churchyard

118

here's full and there's no one to dig the grave. His brother lives at Massinicorvo and he has a plot. It's very difficult for Italians. We can't always bury our dead where they belong.'

The German shrugged and smiled. 'It's difficult for Germans, too, Signora,' he said. 'We would also like to die where we belong. Preferably of old age and in bed. We'd even like to do our living where we belong. Soon though, it will be finished. *Domani sono kaputt.*'

'Amen to that, Signor Soldato.'

They were all tired by the time they were safely into the country, so they drove the hearse off the road and tried to sleep for an hour or two. There were four curtains and, without thinking, Marco, Foscari and old Tassinari took one each, which left one between Pugh and Tamara. The other three seemed to have fallen asleep at once, so they huddled together and wrapped the fourth curtain round them both. By this time neither of them considered it at all odd.

By full daylight they were well south of Vicinamontane and growing in confidence with every step. Near Pozzi Piano, even, a column of German soldiers resting by the roadside was brought to attention by their officer, who slammed up a tremendous salute as the coffin passed. Pugh acknowledged the salute with a lift of Ciasca's top hat.

Ahead of them somewhere was the new front line. The Germans hadn't had time to strengthen it yet, and they knew that if only they could find somewhere to hide they ought to be able to slip past in the next night or so.

'We might have to bribe our way through,' Pugh said.

Marco moaned. 'You talk of giving pictures away as if they were saint's day presents.'

'Which would you rather do? Stay here with them and have the Germans take the lot, or bribe your way through with one and keep the rest?' Pugh's retort reduced Marco to silence.

They stopped for breakfast, which consisted of a handful of bread, a slice of German sausage and a swig of German wine. Then they climbed back on the hearse and set off again – Pugh driving, Tamara with him on the box, Foscari and Marco hanging on the back or walking alongside, and old Tassinari stretched out at full length alongside the flower-decked coffin with the black and silver curtains drawn, trying to recover from a night of sitting upright.

They had entered a range of low hills and were heading now with the sun in their eyes through a strip of wooded country. Large rocks protruded from the poor soil and there were patches of olive grove on either side. The road wound round the shoulder of the hill then began to drop into the valley. Just ahead was a fork with a crude sign painted on the wall – Naples in one direction; Crocifisso in the other, up a narrow stony road.

They had just reached the junction when they heard the roar of an engine from the Crocifisso road, and a truck lifted into view over a rise.

'Germans!' Pugh said. 'Look straight ahead.'

Marco and Foscari dragged Tassinari from the back of the hearse, where he had been happily dreaming of being at home and in bed with the war over and the Germans defeated, shook him to life and held him upright between them as he came to wakefulness, all three of them stumping along on weary feet in a sombre, shabby procession behind the hearse.

The German lorry roared past without stopping, a large crate labelled *Nicht Stuerzen* – Don't drop – in the back, and they were just congratulating themselves on their ruse when a black Mercedes appeared over the same rise. As it passed them, Pugh recognised the man beside the driver as Hoggeimer.

He seemed not to notice them and the car shot past without stopping, and Pugh was just flicking a quick smile at Tamara when he realised the car was slowing down. Glancing over his shoulder, he saw it was pulling to a stop at the side of the road.

'Oh, *Mamma mia*,' Tamara moaned.

The car was reversing at speed. As Pugh drew the horse to a stop Hoggeimer smiled up at him.

'What is this?' he said cheerfully. 'I thought you buried Boccaccio Detto Banti two days ago. Who can this be?'

'Enrichetta,' Tamara said quickly, before Pugh could gather his wits. 'Enrichetta Arsini. She was his house-keeper. For twenty years.'

Marco nodded his agreement. 'Very faithful, Signor Tenente,' he said.

Hoggeimer had climbed from the car now and was walking slowly round the stationary hearse, peering inside it.

'Making away with the curtains, too, I see,' he said cheerfully, indicating the folded bundle beyond the coffin. 'Still, why not? Times are hard and you'll be able to sell them.' He glanced at Tamara. 'They could make a splendid dress for you, Signora. The colour would suit you.'

Tamara went pink and glanced at Pugh. 'That's what my husband said.' His hand felt for hers and she grabbed his fingers and clutched them tightly.

'And what's this?' Hoggeimer was staring at a flat parcel propped against the end of the hearse. 'It wouldn't be one of those missing Detto Bantis that the Herr Kapitän is seeking, would it?'

It was clearly going to be a case of bribery. The suggestion was obvious in Hoggeimer's expression.

'It's not a very good one, Signor Tenente,' Pugh pointed out. 'We thought it wouldn't be missed, and when the others were taken into the vaults of the Palazzo Municipale, we thought we might keep that one for ourselves and held it back. As you say, times aren't easy.'

'So they *are* in the vaults,' Hoggeimer smiled. 'That

121

will please the Herr Kapitän. In the meantime, I think perhaps *I* might have this one.'

'What about us?' Marco demanded hotly.

Hoggeimer smiled. 'Perhaps your government should never have surrendered. When they switched sides it changed things a little. Take it out.'

Pugh scrambled into the hearse to reach the painting. Bringing it out, he handed it as sullenly as he could manage to Hoggeimer, who peeled off the wrapping paper and stared at it.

'What's it called?' he asked.

'*A Farmer Selling a Cow*, Signor Tenente.'

'I've seen better.'

'So have I, Tenente. That's why we thought the Führer wouldn't be interested.'

'He won't be! *His* agents are buying him Canalettos and Tiepolos – though, in fact, his tastes are stunted and he cares more for the cliché-ridden stuff turned out by Buerke and Uhde, or the vulgar nudes of Hans Baldung. I'm different. *I* could use it.'

'I wouldn't hang it over *my* mantelpiece,' Tamara said sharply.

Hoggeimer smiled. 'Neither would I, Signora. I shall sell it. What is it worth?'

'Only a few thousand lire,' Tassinari said.

'Nearer five million I would say. That's worth having in anybody's language.' Hoggeimer smiled, his handsome face creased with mirth.

He rolled the canvas carefully and gestured at the hearse with it. 'I'll not take the hearse. I don't think it's worth much, and you doubtless need it. *Ciao*, Signori, Signora. Enjoy your escape.'

He turned and began to walk back towards his car, the painting under his arm, still smiling, still very satisfied with himself. As he reached the car, he turned, unrolled the painting and studied it again. He was still studying it when the silence was shattered by a tremendous volley of gunfire. It came from among the trees and the rocks

122

about them and lifted Hoggeimer off his feet.

Not knowing who was firing, Pugh grabbed Tamara and pushed her under the hearse. But the bullets weren't coming anywhere near them and when he lifted his head he saw Hoggeimer's body was still rolling across the road, nudged along by the bullets that were ripping into it, until finally it ended head-down in the ditch, the booted feet in the air in a ludicrous manner. The driver of the car, who had been struggling to start the vehicle, had fallen over the side of the door. The painting, ripped and torn by the bullets that had passed through it into Hoggeimer's chest, had skated into the ditch at the opposite side of the road.

For a long time there was utter silence, then they began to hear voices. Raising himself to his knees, Pugh grabbed the reins of the frightened horse as a group of men emerged from the trees and began to straggle down to the road. They wore red armbands and were dressed in a mixture of civilian and military clothing, some of them in flat caps, one or two in the narrow-brimmed feathered hat of the Italian Alpini regiments. They carried a variety of weapons, from sub-machine guns to rifles and pistols, and even shotguns.

Among them was Della Croce, the red-faced student-butcher's boy from Vicinamontane, who was carrying the ancient muzzle-loader Marco Detto Banti had given him.

10

The Italians were clambering over the drystone wall now and jumping across the ditch.

The German driver moaned and moved slightly, and one of them opened the door and drew his pistol. Firing it into the German's head, he kicked the body as it rolled into the road.

'*Tedesco* swine,' he said.

As Tamara hid her face in her hands, Pugh put his arm round her shoulders. Sadism, cruelty and brutality ran through the history of Italy, despite the fact that through the same blood flowed a torrent of love and affection, a mingled current of dark and light that set the Latin soul apart from the rest of the world.

For a long time nobody said anything. Even the birds seemed to have stopped singing. Dust stirred from the road by the bullets was still hanging in the air and there was a smell of new blood and cordite. Marco was standing with his arms held stiffly upwards, a fixed grin on his face. Tassinari was slack-jawed and sick-looking, shocked by the killing, though after four years of war and the air raids on Naples he must have seen plenty already. Foscari had moved behind Pugh and was trying to look as small as possible.

The man who appeared to be the leader of the group was studying the Mercedes. He was a sturdy man, with angry lines on his face, a shock of dark hair and a large moustache. He reminded Pugh of someone he knew.

'I am Salvadori, Giovanni, known as Uragano,' he said, 'chairman of the Crocifisso Branch of the Partito Communisto Italiano,' and Pugh realised that he had deliberately made himself look like the man who was without doubt his hero: Stalin.

'Nobody escaped,' he went on. 'We'll take the motor car and the weapons.' He paused. '*And* their boots and trousers. I don't think anyone will want the rest.'

The dusty surface of the road was puddled with blood but the Italians seemed unmoved. Della Croce passed in front of Pugh, grinning at him. 'Nobody escaped,' he said, repeating the words of his leader. 'And now there will be a gun for me. I can throw this old thing away.'

'I shouldn't,' Pugh advised. 'It's an antique. You'd find a buyer for it among the Americans for certain. They like things as ancient as that. They don't have a lot that's old.'

Della Croce studied the gun then he looked up and nodded. Slinging the gun across his back, he picked up the rifle from alongside the dead driver. Someone else had wrenched Hoggeimer's belt, pistol and holster from his body and was engaged in wiping the blood from them with a piece of dirty rag. Another of the men had tossed aside the battered shoes he wore and was dragging on the lieutenant's shiny boots. Money, watches and trinkets were pushed into ragged pockets.

'There is only one thing for an Italian male,' Della Croce said. 'Revenge. War to the knife. In the resistance we have found our patriotism again.'

'Some men get married,' Pugh pointed out in a flat voice.

'Pah! Italian girls are impossible. Either they're peasants who just want to fill the house with babies, or they are stupid and just want to marry counts. But we're different in the south. In Naples we shot our Fascists. When Rome falls they will form a new government with them. A pity we couldn't get the lorry as well. It means they've got away with *The Adoration of the Lamb* from Crocifisso.' He gestured at the hearse. 'Who's that you've got in there?' he demanded. 'Surely not old Detto Banti?'

They glanced at each other and it was Marco who spoke. His words came out in a rush.

'It's Enrichetta.'

'Enrichetta Arsini?' Della Croce seemed startled. '*Dio*, that was sudden, wasn't it? I saw her only two days ago. What happened?'

'They said it was her heart.'

Salvadori looked at Pugh for the first time. Then he turned to Marco and gestured. 'Who are these people?'

Tassinari answered for Marco. 'I am Avvocato Tassinari from Naples,' he said.

'What are you doing behind the German lines?'

'I am administering the estate of the late Boccaccio Detto Banti, who died four days ago.'

'Was he worth much?' Della Croce asked.

'Nothing.'

Salvadori looked at the others.

'And these?'

'Signorina Detto Banti. Abandoned daughter of Bocco Detto Banti. She would have been heir to his fortune if there had been one to leave to her.'

'He was wealthy?'

'"Was" is the operative word. It was all gone. He hadn't painted for years.'

'I heard there were paintings.'

'Removed to the vaults of the Palazzo Municipale, I heard, Leader,' Della Croce said. 'It was destroyed by German shells as they entered. The Germans are still trying to dig them out.'

'And this man?'

'A British soldier.'

'And this one?'

'An escaped British prisoner of war,' Pugh said quickly, in case the partisans tried to force Foscari to join them.

Foscari nodded speechlessly.

'You can join us if you wish,' Salvadori invited. 'Many have. Deserters from the Italian army. English. German.

126

Russian. We are known as the League of Nations.'

Pugh said nothing. What Salvadori said was right, and it was indicative of the chaos and tragedy of Italy.

The dead driver was dragged away from the Mercedes, and Della Croce climbed into his place, tried the horn and started the engine.

'We could catch the lorry up,' he said. 'And get the Tintoretto back.'

Salvadori frowned. 'Don't be stupid. We're too near Vicinamontane. We'll head back into the hills.' He looked at Pugh. 'You can keep the hearse, Englishman. It's not fast enough for us. Where are you going?'

'Naples.'

'The Germans are in front.'

'We thought we might get through them.'

'There's a gap between Crocifisso and Vermagna. At Bagnano. If you go by Moccino you might get through. But you'll need to hurry before the *tedeschi* close it. The Anglo-Americans are regrouping to push them back. We heard by radio. We're going to meet them.'

As they talked, Della Croce was turning the car round.

'We've been told to ambush anything we see,' Salvadori went on. 'The Americans are going to send aircraft to drop weapons and plastic explosive. To blow bridges.' He grinned and raised a clenched fist. 'Long live Communist Italy!'

As Della Croce finished his manoeuvres with the car, the resistance men clambered aboard, clinging to the running boards like flies on a jam-pot. Della Croce tooted the horn again and the car moved off with such a jerk two of the men fell off. There were shouts, Salvadori slapped at Della Croce and the car stopped. The two men picked themselves up and climbed aboard again, and this time the Mercedes moved away slowly, picking up speed, until it disappeared over the hump in the road to Crocifisso, where they had first seen it climbing into sight.

For a long time, the five people standing by the hearse said nothing. Tamara still had her hands to her face, frozen and mute with shock. Pugh touched her shoulder and she swung round and buried her face in his chest. For a while he stood with his arms round her, then she pushed herself free.

Non c'è niente,' she said with an effort. 'Far worse things than this are happening every day in Italy. And they were Germans and we are unhurt.' She essayed a look in the direction of Hoggeimer. Bluebottles had already arrived and were feasting on the blood. Her face twisted. 'Can we bury them?' she asked.

There was a spade strapped on the underside of the hearse. Clearly at times, Agente di Pompe Funebri Ciasca had been obliged not only to attend the last rites for his clients, he had also been obliged to dig their graves. Working one after the other, Pugh, Foscari and Marco managed to scrape a shallow grave in which they placed the two bodies side by side. Covering them up, they placed stones on top. By the time they had finished, Tassinari had fashioned a crude cross by tying together with the yellow curtain cords two pieces of wood he had found among the trees. They planted it at the head of the grave and Tassinari muttered something over it.

As they turned away, they saw Tamara on her knees in the road, studying the remains of the painting. The bullets had cut straight across it, destroying it completely. Only one fragment, the head of the farmer who had been selling his cow, was worth saving, and she borrowed a knife from Pugh to cut it free.

'I think I'd like to keep it,' she said slowly. 'After all, it is a Detto Banti and he was my father. Perhaps it still has some value.'

'Probably more than before,' Tassinari said. 'With the history it's just acquired.'

'We'd better go,' Pugh urged.

'We'd better also have another picture to barter for our lives,' Tassinari suggested quietly.

Pugh glanced round at the others. Only Marco objected.

'We've lost *one*,' he said.

'I would say it was worth it,' Tassinari pointed out calmly. 'Without it, we might all have been heading back towards Vicinamontane behind the lieutenant's car. And you know what the Germans do to people who steal art treasures.'

They drove towards the trees and, pulling off the road, Foscari unscrewed the lid of the coffin and removed a second canvas. They had foreseen the possibility of the need for more than one and had placed them in order, with what Tassinari and Pugh had considered the worst ones at the top. Pugh looked at the back of the canvas. It was another allegory. It consisted of a crucified Christ at the top of the picture with, at the bottom, a scene of warfare with armoured soldiers moving about with flags.

'*Prince of Peace*,' he read. He looked at Marco. 'Bocco was in a cynical frame of mind when he painted this,' he said.

Since the wrapping from the *Farmer Selling A Cow* was covered with Hoggeimer's blood, they decided to use the new picture as part of the decoration of the hearse, because it was far from unusual for Italian hearses to be placarded with religious pictures.

Foscari screwed up the coffin again and they propped the picture by the glass doors. With the flowers hiding the bottom half, it looked like a straightforward representation of the crucified Christ.

As they closed the doors, they decided to take a rest for food. Foscari unharnessed the old horse and tethered it to a tree so that it could graze, and as it wrenched at the grass, the rest of them sat in a silent huddle and ate the rest of the bread and sausage and finished the wine.

The sun was warm and Marco, still sullen, was just stretching out for a doze when they heard the sound of an engine. It was the Mercedes returning. This time it contained only Salvadori, Della Croce and two other men. Della Croce was grinning all over his red face. As the car halted, he jumped out and, followed by Salvadori, marched straight up the slope to where the hearse stood.

Immediately, he spotted the canvas propped up by the rear door. He turned to Salvadori and gestured with his thumb.

'That's a Detto Banti,' he said. He grinned at Marco. 'I thought you'd try to get away with one of them.'

'We tried to get away with two,' Tassinari snapped.

'Where's the other?'

'You destroyed it.' The old lawyer reached into the hearse and produced all that was left of the *Farmer Selling a Cow*. 'It no longer has any value.'

Della Croce was opening the doors of the hearse. 'They used to say a Detto Banti would fetch a million lire.'

'Four million, in fact,' Tassinari commented.

'That will buy guns for the party's action group.' Salvadori turned to Della Croce and swung a flat hand at him. *'Idiota! Cretino!* 'why didn't you warn us of the value of these paintings? We might have saved them both. That would have meant twice as many guns, twice as many comrades armed.'

'I never thought!'

'Comrades are expected to think.'

Della Croce placed the canvas reverently on the rear seat of the Mercedes, then they all climbed in after it and drove away.

Marco stared after them, his face a picture of fury and indignation. 'Two,' he said.

11

They were all gloomy and low in spirits.

'Two,' Marco kept saying. 'Two.'

Tamara was less concerned with the loss of the paintings than with the loss of life. 'Italy is descending into anarchy,' she said. 'There is no law anywhere.'

Pugh said nothing because he suspected that there would be no real law in Italy for some time after the Germans had been sent packing.

They were on the point of moving on when Tassinari reminded them about the paintings. 'We shall now need another within easy reach,' he said. 'We may have to bribe our way across the lines and we mustn't have to pull the lot out and choose one there.'

They agreed. A painting had freed them from the Germans and from Salavadori's partisans, but they all knew that if either Hoggeimer or Salvadori had been aware that there were other canvasses in the hearse, they would have lost the lot.

It was late, so they decided to leave the rest of the paintings where they were in the coffin and open it the following morning. Because it was drizzling, the first essential was to find somewhere they could rest for the night.

'There's an orphanage at Moccino,' Tamara said. 'The Convent of the Virgin of Manimora. The nuns will give us somewhere to sleep.'

They climbed back to their places, Pugh, Tamara and Tassinari on the box of the hearse, the other two riding in the back with the doors open, their feet dangling. Tassinari was in a contemplative mood.

'You know,' he said, 'I have often wondered what Bocco was up to with these paintings.'

'You think they're fakes?'

Tassinari shrugged. 'In the past the masters didn't regard forgery as a depreciation of their work. They showed indulgence towards such frauds and even promoted them. Boucher always permitted the copying of his pictures and even signed the best with his own name. If Ingres judged a copy good he signed it, making it an original. Corot did the same. He only painted 2,000 pictures but there are more than 5,000 in existence. Utrillo couldn't distinguish forgeries from his own work and Vlaminck was said once to have painted a picture in the style of Cézanne which Cézanne thought was his own. Rembrandt, in his *Christ Scourging the Money Changers*, copied the figure of Christ from a woodcut by Dürer, while Rubens, one of the shrewdest men in the business, copied paintings of 200 years earlier and signed copies of his work painted by his pupils.'

Tassinari smiled as he went on. 'The Louvre paid a fortune for a 300-year-old Benvieni bust in the last century, and ignored a dealer who said it was only three years old. Van Goghs by the dozen were exposed as forgeries in 1929 but Meier Graef, in Germany, whose opinions on Van Gogh were held in awe, continued to be convinced by them. Now' – he shrugged again – 'there are probably dozens of works being painted at this very moment especially to be bought up by Hitler's agents on his behalf. He knows nothing about art and manages to pick agents who also know nothing.'

He nodded to the clopping hooves of the horse. 'I've stood in the Uffizi Galleries,' he said, 'watching students copying the masters, and have not been able to tell the difference. The sole reason for forgery is because purchasers judge paintings by the name on them. Art has become a status symbol.'

'All of which,' Pugh reminded him, 'doesn't help us choose another Detto Banti.'

It brought them back to earth with a bang and they finally decided to keep out the painting of sheep being driven up a hill by a shepherd, entitled *Sheep Returning to the Fold.*

'Nothing but a lot of sheeps' behinds,' Pugh commented. 'On the other hand, sheep facing you aren't exactly an inspiration either.'

Marco was far from pleased. 'This is the third,' he pointed out angrily. 'At this rate, our 48 million lire worth of art is going to look pretty sick. It's already down to 40 million.'

Tamara sniffed. Her opinion of Marco seemed to have undergone a certain amount of change. 'I think I could live on that for a while,' she said.

The Convent and Orphanage of the Virgin of Manimora at Moccino was at the end of a long valley marked by the tall brush strokes of cypresses and rows of terraced vines. It was a huge edifice consisting of wings containing offices, dining rooms, work rooms and living quarters, making the four sides of a huge square which contained a well and a few trees for shade against the summer sun. It had existed for 200 years and had always opened its doors to travellers.

At the moment, the courtyard was noisy with the cries of children. One nun was overseeing a group of little girls manipulating a skipping rope and another, younger and more boisterous, was keeping goal between two heaps of piled coats for a shrieking horde of small boys who were playing football with a tied-up bundle of rags. As they pushed their noses inside the gate, she had just collected the 'ball' and was returning it to centre field with a tremendous kick from one of her stout black boots.

The nun who received them agreed that they could remain there for the night, and they drove the hearse into the courtyard. Seeing the coffin, the nuns crossed themselves and muttered prayers for the deceased.

Tamara was on the point of admitting there was nothing inside it but rocks and a few rolled canvasses, when Pugh whipped her away quickly.

'For God's sake,' he whispered. 'Don't tell them!'

'But they think we've got a body in there.'

'It won't harm them.'

'But they're nuns! They believe in truth, honesty and God the Father, God the Son and God the Holy Ghost.'

'They'll be no worse off for not knowing.'

Tassinari was busily telling the sister who had welcomed them a long story about his uncle who had died in Vicinamontane but, because of the arrival of the Germans, couldn't be buried there and had to be taken to Moccino.

'He was Boccaccio Detto Banti, the painter,' he explained gravely.

The nun had obviously heard the name. She crossed herself and suggested that they place the coffin in the chapel for the night. Tassinari clearly hadn't expected this but there was nothing he could do about it. They wrestled the box out of the hearse and carried it solemnly into the spartan little chapel, where two benches had been placed near the altar to support it.

Pugh was about to turn away when Tamara clutched his wrist. 'Prayers,' she whispered, horrified. 'Prayers for the dead!'

Pugh pushed Foscari ahead of him and they knelt with her and the other two while the nun muttered at the foot of the coffin.

'I feel awful,' Tamara whispered. 'I am a fraud. I don't like it.'

'We'll be gone tomorrow.'

As they were shown their quarters, Marco introduced them all, announcing Pugh and Tamara by the names they'd been given by Tassinari at Vicinamontane when Klemper had arrived.

The nun didn't bat an eyelid. 'I am Sister Angelica,' she said. She indicated a large room, where several

134

straw mattresses were spread on the stone floor, and led Pugh and Tamara to another smaller room further down the corridor, where there was a proper bed. It consisted of a battered iron bedstead with a thin horsehair mattress, a bolster and two folded blankets.

'This is for visitors,' she said. 'It's the best we have to offer,' she admitted with a smile. 'But for a loving wife and husband, I imagine it will be enough.'

As she turned away, Pugh saw Tamara opening her mouth and promptly whipped her round and kissed her so she could say nothing. From the doorway the nun saw them and beamed.

'We can provide you with a meal,' she said. 'It won't be much. Largely vegetable soup and bread, but it will help you on your way.'

As the door closed, Tamara wrenched herself free. Swinging her arm, she delivered a tremendous swipe at Pugh's face. As he stepped back she almost fell over.

'They're nuns!' she said furiously. 'I'm not going to sleep here with you!'

'You don't have to sleep *with* me. Just here. It's very different.'

'They think we're married.'

'You're certainly behaving as if we are.'

The chiding seemed to bring her up sharp. 'Piu,' she said, 'we can't do this to these good women.'

Pugh thought for a moment before answering. 'Nuns,' he said, 'have always seemed to me to be very down-to-earth people. Witness the one who was playing goalkeeper. If there's one thing they've learned to do it's survive. If they knew, I doubt if they'd worry. They'd understand. Most of them do.'

'Then why don't we tell them?'

'And let them know that we've allowed them to put the coffin in their chapel and say prayers over it? Let's spare them the truth. It's best to say nothing.'

She studied him for a long time, her face grave. 'I think, Piu,' she said, 'that you are dishonest.'

135

The meal was sparse, as they had been warned: thin vegetable soup with bread. They ate in the main dining room with the children and the nuns who were looking after them. The tables were scrubbed and devoid of anything but knives and spoons, with tin mugs for the wine that was served in earthenware pitchers.

The children were noisy and full of laughter and chatter. From time to time one of the nuns shushed them and they became quiet, but it didn't last long and a moment later they were all noisily chirruping once more.

Sister Angelica sat at the end of the table, smiling benignly on Pugh and Tamara. 'Forty of them,' she said. 'Orphans, every one of them. Children whose fathers have been killed by the war, whose parents have died in the bombing or abandoned them to us because they could no longer feed them. I think they are as happy as they can be. They are given love, a little discipline and a respect for the Church and for the Lord. When we send them out into the world they are no worse for their stay here.'

'How do you manage for money?' Tamara asked anxiously.

'We manage. We have our own little workshops and our sisters are very clever with their hands. One is a carpenter and does the woodwork repairs. We have a bakery. A garden. An orchard. A kitchen. We even have a wheelwright. Sister Domenica is far from expert, but her father was a wheelwright, so she knows what to do and she repairs our carts when they break down.'

'But money, Sister? You must need so much of it.'

Sister Angelica smiled. 'It is often difficult and sometimes we have to cut our rations. We try not to cut the children's so we go a little short ourselves. Not much. Just a little.'

'If only we could give you money!'

'Nobody in Italy these days has money, child. We would welcome money from anywhere for the children, but when it doesn't exist we simply manage without.'

They spent the evening sitting in the courtyard, where Foscari joined in the football, and as darkness fell they went to their rooms. Tamara refused to look at Pugh and sat with her back to him, avoiding his eyes so that he couldn't tell whether she was angry or not.

'*Sono truffatrice,*' she said. 'I am a cheat. We're taking their food and doing nothing for them.' She paused, then she swung round. 'Why can't we give them a picture, Piu? It would be so simple. We could give them a canvas and tell them where to sell it. It would bring in enough money to keep forty children for months.'

Pugh was not unattracted by the idea and knew it was part of her generous spirit to think of it. But there were drawbacks.

'How do we do it?'

'We have one in the coffin. The sheeps' behinds.'

'How do we get it out without letting them know the coffin doesn't contain a body?'

She stamped her foot. 'You are too practical, Piu,' she snapped, but it was obvious she realised he was right.

She refused to lie on the bed with him, so he lay down alone and left her sitting upright on the opposite edge. About midnight, he woke to see her still there, her body drooping, her head dangling, her fair hair over her face like the wing of a bright bird. She was fast asleep, kept upright by some interior mental plumb-line. Without speaking, he put gentle hands on her and laid her down on the bed, then placed the blanket over her. She managed to open her eyes for a second but she was so tired she didn't know what was happening and simply murmured a quiet 'Grazie, Piu,' before falling asleep again.

He woke up in the morning to find her sitting bolt upright again, on the bed alongside him, her eyes flashing with a dark fire of indignation.

'You made me go to bed with you,' she said.

He shook his head. 'If I hadn't, you'd probably have

fallen off your perch on to your head and stunned yourself.'

She refused to speak to him and they went silently to the big dining room for breakfast with the others, the children streaming noisily past them. The meal consisted of nothing but coffee and dry bread, and once again Tamara flushed pink with embarrassment at the knowledge that in the hearse they had canvasses that were probably worth millions of lire while the nuns were struggling to feed the orphans on nothing.

'We must do something,' she insisted in an urgent, demanding whisper to Pugh.

They attended another session in the chapel. Tamara was silent, watching the praying nuns.

'Sancta Maria, Madre di Dio, prega per noi peccatori, adesso e nell' ora della nostra morte. . . .'

The altar glowed with candles, gilt, cheap polished brass and the glittering of imitation gems. She adjusted the black lace scarf she wore on her head, deep in thought.

'Ave Maria, gratia plena, Dominus tecum. . . .'

She rose with the others, crossing herself with quick dabs of the fingers against her breast. As they left the chapel, Sister Angelica drew Pugh on one side.

'Your uncle,' she said. 'He could be buried here. We have a little graveyard where the nuns are buried when they are old and die.' Her face became sad. 'Sometimes there are children. Since the war started, too many, unhappily. I think we could find room.'

Pugh went into a long explanation involving Tassinari and a family plot that existed in Moccino. Sister Angelica didn't argue and they solemnly carried the coffin back to the hearse. The horse, Fiorello, was led out of the stable, where he had spent the night with the three mules the nuns kept for doing the heavy work about the fields they tilled, and backed into the shafts of the hearse. The sable plumes still attached to his browband bobbed and nodded as they moved slowly

138

through the gate of the orphanage. The children halted their games to wave them off. It brought tears to Tamara's eyes.

'We must do something,' she said furiously. 'We have 40 million lire-worth of painting in the hearse. Surely we can afford to give away one canvas to the nuns.'

'No,' Marco said.

'Yes,' she insisted. 'And if you are not prepared to do something about it, I am. I shall send one to them as soon as they become mine.'

They had just entered the woods a mile from the convent when there was a bump as the rear wheel hit a stone, then a clatter and a lurch which threw Marco and Foscari from their perches at the rear. Fiorello came to a dignified stop, his head up proudly for a moment before it began to droop to its normal position between his forelegs.

'The wheel has come off, sir,' Foscari said.

The hearse was tilted crazily to the right, the wheel in the ditch at the roadside, and they stood staring at it, wondering what to do.

'Sir, I regret to announce that the split pin's worn through.'

'So how do we keep the wheel on?'

Foscari smiled. 'The convent, sir,' he said. 'They have a resident wheelright there. She will have a split pin, or if not a split pin, an oak peg we can drive through in its place.'

'We're not going back there,' Marco said.

Tamara rounded on him angrily. 'Yes, we are,' she said. 'And we're going to take them a picture and tell them where to sell it.'

Marco moaned. '*È finito!*' he said, slapping at his forehead with the heel of his hand. 'Give away my birthright!'

'*My* birthright,' she corrected.

'Your birthright! My birthright! Anybody's birth-

139

right! But give it away? Why did I go to all that trouble to dig all those pictures out? Why did we crate them up? Why did we uncrate them, take them from their frames and build a coffin for them? To give them away, of course!'

'It's only the backsides of a lot of sheep going up a hill,' she snapped. 'That one we shan't miss. I should never want to hang that in my living room.'

'Some American from Idaho might! Perhaps he doesn't know that the sheep's backsides are not very good, only that it was painted by Bocco Detto Banti and is worth a lot of money. In Idaho if you have a Detto Banti in the dining room – or a Canaletto on the stairs, or anything else – you are one up on the neighbours.'

'We are giving them the sheeps' backsides!'

'No.'

'*Sì!*'

Pugh watched the duel with amusement. While he couldn't recommend Tamara's generosity with something that wasn't yet hers, he could only admire her warm heart.

Curiously, old Tassinari seemed to agree. No one raised any support for Marco, and in the end they accepted what Tamara insisted. Unscrewing the coffin, they removed the *Sheep Returning to the Fold*.

It was Pugh and Tamara who set off for help. It seemed safe to leave the hearse and the other paintings with Foscari to guard them. Without him, Pugh would have expected to find Marco gone on their return, the paintings stolen and old Tassinari unconscious by the roadside. But Foscari was sturdy enough to deal with Marco, whose drinking had hardly left him in the best of health, and by this time Foscari was devoted to Pugh and unlikely to be bribed or duped.

Tamara walked with the rolled painting in her hand, her brows down, her eyes angry. 'We must do it,' she said.

'We're doing it,' Pugh reminded her gently. 'Just as you wished.'

She stopped and faced him. 'You don't mind, Piu?'

'They're your paintings. Not yet, of course, but they will be. It's your own property you're giving away.'

'They're so brave and so poor. And I don't think you approve'.

'As a lawyer protecting your property, I don't. As a sergeant in Field Security sent to deliver the Detto Bantis to the British Government, I don't. But as someone who sees a kind heart, you have my full approval.'

She grinned at him, then her face fell again. 'What about your officer? Will he not be angry that you have not brought them all?'

By this time Pugh was convinced that Tasker's interest in the paintings was entirely personal, and he had been wondering for some time how to keep them out of his sight until he could check on the Government's interest. He didn't like Tasker, who, he felt, was merely feathering his own nest. He couldn't imagine managing to get him sent home in disgrace – much as he would have liked to – but he could at least thwart him. On the other hand, that thought prompted another. If he thwarted Tasker, Tasker would probably seek vengeance and he, Pugh, would probably end up in a foxhole in a jungle somewhere, being shot at by Japanese snipers.

The nuns were surprised to see them back, but delighted to be of help.

Sister Domenica, who ran the stables, had no split pins because no one had seen a split pin in that part of Italy since the beginning of the war, but she produced an oak wedge which she promised could be hammered home in place of it, and even offered to help them do it.

Despite their protests, she passed them over to Sister Angelica, who, hearing Tamara's wish to make a gift, led

141

them at once to see the Mother Superior, a middle-aged woman with a gently resolute face and a large bunch of keys. As they sat down on chairs of a hardness only the Catholic Church could devise, Tamara had an uplifted look on her face and, as permission was granted for their help to be given, she produced the painting of the *Sheep Returning to the fold.*

'We would like to give you this,' she said.

The Mother Superior's eyes widened. 'That is very beautiful,' she said, and Pugh decided that she didn't know a lot about art. 'We will have Sister Monica frame it and it can be hung in the dining room'

'No, no!' Tamara protested. 'You mustn't hang it! You must sell it! It has value! It might even be a painting by Boccaccio Detto Banti.'

Sister Angelica lifted her hands. 'In that case, it *must* go on the dining room wall! To remind us of your generosity!

'No! Please!' Tamara was growing desperate. She was trying hard to put money in their hands and they could think of nothing else but to hang it on the wall.

'It would beautify the orphanage.'

'But that's not the point,' Tamara said. 'We have found one or two of these pictures. They are the work of my uncle and we are taking them to Naples. And you have been so kind, and you work so hard for the children and do so much with so little, we want you to change it for money. So that you can buy food and clothing for the children.'

The Mother Superior smiled and glanced at Sister Angelica. 'I think perhaps, Sister,' she said gently, 'that in this case we must accept the gift in the nature it was intended. As an addition to our funds.' She looked at Pugh. 'But I know nothing about art. How much is it worth?'

'Over a million lire, Reverend Mother,' Tamara blurted out. 'Perhaps four million.'

The Mother Superior looked shocked. 'Then we can't possibly take it.'

'You must! It is mine! I'm giving it to you!'

The Mother Superior looked at Pugh, who shrugged. 'I'm a lawyer,' he said. 'Of sorts,' he added. 'And I know about art because I was once a painter. My advice is to take the painting and sell it as soon as you can. Detto Bantis have a value now but they'll probably not retain it.'

'How do I sell it? And where?'

Pugh thought of Da Sangalla and De Castro, even of Tasker and Baracca.

'I think I can send you customers,' he said. 'Just as soon as it's possible. But before I go, if you will provide me with pen and paper, Avvocato Tassinari and I will draw up a form of sale.'

'Why?'

'Because we can't guarantee the painting is genuine.'

'Then I can't sell it as genuine.'

'You must sell it simply as a painting, Reverend Mother, and leave your customer to make up his own mind. Tell him you know nothing of art. That would be honest, and I still think you'll find that someone will buy it without question. And if he finds he is wrong and it isn't what he thought it was, he will try to sell it to someone else. So you needn't fear.'

'It sounds dishonest.'

'The art world is ruthless and often less than honest. You will be doing nothing dishonest if you say nothing, and if, as I suspect, the people who will try to buy it *are* dishonest, then it will be their loss, not yours.'

The Mother Superior smiled. 'I think you know a great deal about the business of art, young man.'

'I wish I did, Reverend Mother. I've just seen the way it operates. And, if I might say so, if you could manage to frame the painting it will look very much better.'

The Mother Superior looked at Sister Angelica. 'We have the picture of the Adoration of the Magi,' she said. 'It is not very good. In fact, I would go so far as to say it's very bad. I think we'll have Sister Domenica take it out of its frame and replace it with this. Then' – she beamed

143

at Pugh and Tamara – 'then we'll wait for customers.'

Outside, Tamara turned to Pugh with huge delighted eyes. 'Oh, Piu,' she said. *'Buono, gentile* Piu, I think you are splendid. So *simpatico.* So helpful.'

Impulsively she reached up and kissed him. Then she blushed and turned away. 'One of these days,' she said, 'God will punish me for my impulsiveness. *Non è vero?'* She paused. 'Why did you take such care with the document of sale for the Reverend Mother?'

'It would be pointless giving them a picture and then having someone swindle them for it.'

'You not only told her the price to ask – and not to move from – you also wrote a document which would prevent a buyer demanding his money back if the picture were found to be a forgery. Do you think it *is* a forgery?'

'It hasn't been seen by an expert yet.'

'And if it is?'

'Then, if the Reverend Mother offers no promises or advice or suggestions, no one can claim she has swindled anyone. I also told her to make sure that she has the priest from Moccino present, together with Sister Angelica and Sister Domenica, so that she has witnesses to what is said.'

She looked at him shrewdly. 'I think you are *expecting* someone dishonest to try to buy the picture.'

'I think I am.'

'And that he will try to buy it at a knock-out price?'

'Knock-down's the word. But, yes, that's true.'

'But he will be someone who is shrewd enough – or shall I say crooked enough – if he finds he has paid too much for it, to be able to sell it again at a profit.'

'Exactly.'

'To someone who will think he has got a bargain.'

'You have it in one.'

'Who is this so dishonest buyer?'

Pugh smiled, thinking of Da Sangalla, De Castro,

144

Baracca, Tasker, and doubtless a few more too. 'There are a lot of them around,' he said.

II

1

The nuns gave them a map and marked off what they knew of the German positions. The Italian Church had seen so many invaders in its long history it had learned how to be realistic about war.

'They are along here,' Sister Angelica said, her finger running along the sheet. 'And here, in these barns. But there are still none in Bagnano. We know, because we take great care to learn where they are. They killed one of our sisters by mistake when they first came. It was growing dark and they thought in her habit she was a *marocchino*. They apologised and the officer sent us money and food, but we've been very careful ever since.'

They repaired the wheel and set off again in the afternoon. By the time they approached Bagnano it was growing dark. The weather had changed and the croaking of frogs and the chirping of crickets, normally so deafening, had suddenly become muted. The wind began to whip coldly along the mountainside, and below them to the right, where a stream tumbled over a bed of large white pebbles, they could hear the hiss and clatter of the water over the stones. Sagging from the sky were dark clouds, trailing wispy tendrils into the valleys.

Fiorello was moving in fine style, slapping down his great feet as if he were enjoying himself, but they were all tired and dirty and looking forward to a rest. On either side of them they could hear the thumb and mutter of guns, and occasionally a Very light soared into the blackness. But the area was quiet, as though the Germans, having returned to it, were beginning to regret their hasty action and were considering retreating again. A machine gun tapped in the distance.

The village of Bagnano was deserted. It seemed unbelievable that no one was there, but there were no lights and they could only guess that the villagers had left and that neither the Germans nor the Allies had yet occupied it. They stopped for a while in the main street in the shadow of the church, and Pugh passed round a bottle of brandy the nuns had given them. It was raw stuff and caused them to catch their breath, but it warmed their stomachs and seemed to take the bite out of the wind.

Unexpectedly, it started raining. As they halted by a fork in the road it was falling in black cascades and Tassinari, Marco and Foscari climbed inside the hearse and lay down alongside the coffin. Pugh tried to make Tamara join them but she refused.

'If you can endure it, Piu,' she said, 'so can I.'

By this time they were close to the line and Pugh was worried someone might have heard them, might even be laying an ambush. As he flipped the reins, the old horse leaned against the harness and the hearse began to move again.

Every moment, he expected to run into German soldiers with guns, or trenches or barbed wire, but nothing appeared. Then he began to worry about land mines and insisted on Tamara climbing into the back of the hearse with the others. If the old horse trod on one, at least there would now be only one victim – Fiorello. On the other hand – the thought frightened him – if the old horse's great plodding hooves missed the mine and it was a wheel that ran over it, the ramshackle wooden hearse would save nobody.

As the door slammed, a figure appeared alongside him. It was Foscari. 'I have decided to accompany the Signore Sergente, 'he announced.

As they set off again there was an explosion over on their right somewhere. It made Pugh jump and he felt the tug on the reins as the horse's head jerked up.

Immediately four more explosions occurred and each flash seemed nearer than the last.

'A salvo,' Foscari said. 'The *tedeschi* are trying to find the road. They will come again.'

A machine gun had begun to hammer nervously, and another Very light appeared in the sky, making the rain look like slanting silver rods. The firing soon stopped, though, and Pugh jerked at the reins so that the old horse began to step out again. But the bangs had made him nervous and he was tossing his head and snorting. Sitting in the silence, unspeaking, both Pugh and Foscari were on edge, waiting for the crash of an explosion or the shattering sound of a Schmeisser.

'I wonder how much longer, sir?' Foscari said unexpectedly.

'How much longer what?'

'How much longer everything. This. The weather. The war. *Che desolazione! Santissima Madonna*, I think I'd give a lot to be snug indoors listening to the rain beating on the window.'

Without speaking, Pugh passed him the brandy bottle and he took a swig from it and passed it back.

'We must be nearly through by now,' he said. 'We're well past Bagnano.'

Pugh had a much vaguer idea of where they were but he let the horse find its own way forward through the darkness. If they had managed to proceed in a straight line, he decided, they must surely be somewhere near the Allies' outposts. Perhaps they ought to give some warning of their approach or they might get a gutful of Bren bullets.

'Hallo!' he yelled. 'Hallo! Anyone ahead?'

Unexpectedly Tassinari's old thin voice joined his from the back of the hearse. 'Hello, English,' he was shouting. 'Please not to shoot at us. We are your friends!'

They had just reached the brow of a low hill with a long winding road sloping away below them, and for a moment they waited, listening for a reply. Instead they heard a distant thump and a whistle.

'Oh, Christ,' Pugh said, and the next second there was the crash and flash of an explosion.

The old horse, already nervous, leapt up in the shafts, almost fell on its side as it came down on all fours, and started to whinny. A split second later there was another explosion, much nearer, then another and another, and Pugh felt grit whipping against his skin and smelled the cordite. The last shell seemed to remove his hair, then he was clinging to the box seat as the reins were wrenched from his hands and the old horse set off at a gallop down the slope.

Yelling at Foscari to hang on, he became aware that the darkness was lifting. The stars were fading in a pale sky and the rain was stopping as the clouds moved round the mountains. A few objects were becoming visible as they clattered past. A tree. A broken building. A low stone wall.

Fiorello was well into his stride now. From the back of the hearse they could her Tamara shrieking and the shouts of Marco and old Tassinari. The shelling had stopped but another Very light was hanging in the sky. The machine gun had started hammering again and they could see the tracers shooting past like coloured rockets. They seemed to be aimed at the hearse.

Sliding from one end of the driver's box to the other and back again as the hearse rattled round the corners, Pugh couldn't make out how they stayed on the road. The surface was dreadful, full of stones and pot-holes, so that the vehicle leapt and swayed, and there seemed to be a permanent space between the box and his behind. Foscari was yelling with fright and they could still hear the screams from behind them.

'Whoa, you bastard!' Pugh roared, only half expecting any result, but Fiorello's head was up and he looked as though nothing but a six-inch shell would halt him. Fortunately, there was no more firing, but how the swaying hearse negotiated the corners it was impossible to say. Then the reins, falling across the horse's lifting hindquarters, suddenly flipped up and Pugh managed to catch them. Dragging on them, he yelled to Foscari to help, and the two of them leaned back, heaving with all their strength.

At first it seemed to make no difference but gradually the pace began to diminish and the corners became less dangerous. The last one seemed to be particularly tight, however, and as they approached it, they heard a voice shouting a challenge. There was the flash of a rifle, and a bullet struck the box just below Pugh's backside. As it did so, the old horse seemed to swerve, and the hearse's wheel bounced from the surface of the road into a pothole, jumped out, then slid into the ditch so that the whole contraption subsided half on its side. Still holding the reins, Pugh and Foscari rolled off the box into the ditch.

As the noise stopped, Foscari seemed to be sitting on Pugh's head. Pushing him aside, Pugh heard querulous shouts as the back of the hearse emptied. Foscari sat up, rubbing his elbow.

'Holy Mother of God,' he said.

'God damn the bloody horse!' Pugh said in loud indignation. 'I didn't think it could run that fast!'

To his surprise a voice answered him.

'Who the fuckin' 'ell do you think you are?'

'Pugh!' Pugh's voice was shaking with relief, and from the ordeal of the wild dash down the hill. 'Sergeant Pugh! Field Security! With four Italian civilians!'

'And a fuckin' 'orse an' cart, by the sound of it. What the Christ are you at?'

Pugh stared about him. 'Where are you?'

'Never you mind. Just you stay where you are, mate, until we can 'ave a look at you.'

As they scrambled to their feet they saw the old horse, lathered with sweat and foam, its flanks heaving, trembling in the shafts of the hearse. One of them was splintered but otherwise, apart from the fact that Foscari's coffin lay half out of the rear door, the vehicle seemed intact. Tamara appeared, helping Tassinari, then Marco, running down the hill.

'I fell out,' he explained.

A moment later, figures rose out of the ground round them and a rifle was poked almost up Pugh's nose.

'You're not a sergeant,' the owner said. 'You're a bloody civvy.'

'Don't kid yourself, old son,' Pugh said breathlessly. 'I'm as much in this war as you are.'

After pushing the coffin back in place, they were taken to a sergeant wearing the armband of a military policeman. He was in a broken-down house, sitting at a table with a hurricane lamp.

'They say they're our lot,' the sentry said. 'They've got an 'earse out there wi' a fuckin' coffin in it.'

The sergeant looked up, his eyes suspicious. 'What's all this then?' He sounded like a London bobby confronting a burglar.

His manner irritated Pugh and his quick temper rose at once. 'What's it look like?' he said.

'It looks like a funeral. You've got a hearse and a coffin. But people don't usually ride inside with the corpse.'

'There isn't a corpse,' Pugh said.

'So why have you got a coffin?'

'Because it contains something I was sent to collect and this was the only way we had of transporting it.'

The sergeant looked suspicious. 'What are you doing in civvies?'

'It happened to be part of my job.'

'I've heard that one before. I expect you're adrift. Let's have your name, rank and number.'

Pugh gave them.

'Unit?'

Pugh produced his papers and the warrant card that allowed him to conduct investigations wherever he

154

wished. The sergeant studied it silently for a while.

'Okay,' he said sourly. 'So you're Field Security. But what are doing? What you got in that hearse?'

'What I've got in the hearse is the business of the British Government.'

'As high as that? Who is it? Mussolini?'

'It's not a who. It's a what.'

The sergeant was intrigued and suddenly more friendly, suspecting it was some sort of secret weapon they'd stolen from behind the German lines.

'They reckon they've got pilotless planes ready,' he said. 'Or radio-controlled bombs. They hit some of our ships at Anzio. Is it one of them?'

'As a matter of fact,' Pugh said, 'they're Italian paintings wanted by the Government.'

'In a hearse?'

'A hearse was the only way of getting them away from the Germans and the odd Italians, British and Americans who have an eye on them and probably have a great deal more power than I have.'

The sergeant's face was disbelieving.

'Okay.' He gestured at the other four. 'So where do this lot come in?'

'My assistants. One of them, in fact, is an Italian soldier who's decided he's had enough of fighting for the teds.'

The sergeant frowned. 'Italian soldiers are supposed to report at once – complete with name, rank and number, so they can be properly directed to where they ought to go. What's his name?'

'Enzio Foscari. He's been a great help, and he stays with me.'

The sergeant listened with some scepticism. 'He'd better see the personal officer all the same,' he said. 'He's got a room in the Velasco Palace down the road.' He gestured at the other three. 'And what about them?'

'Also Italians.'

'Doing what?'

155

'Also assisting me in the recovery of Italian art treasures.'

'How?'

Pugh was growing bored with the sergeant's insistence. 'I doubt if you've ever heard of him,' he said. 'But they're all relations of Boccaccio Detto Banti.'

'Who's he when he's at home?'

'Your education, old boy,' Pugh said, 'has been sadly neglected. He's an Anglo-Italian painter of roughly the same calibre as Dante Gabriel Rossetti.'

'And who might *he* be?'

'Oh, Christ, man, give it a rest! He was a famous poet and painter of a similar Anglo-Italian background. The Italian Government decided that Detto Banti was an Italian but the British Government's decided' – I hope, he thought – 'that he's British. They therefore want the pictures he left, as part of the art heritage of the British nation. I was ordered to collect them. I was stranded behind the German lines by the attack near Vicinamontane'.

'That'll be why you're short of a uniform?'

'That's exactly why I'm short of a uniform.'

'You'd better get one as fast as you can.' The sergeant wasn't giving much away in the manner of comradeship. 'You'd better report to the office over there.'

'What office?'

'The provost marshal's office. You'll want to contact someone, won't you, to take the pictures off your hands.'

It had been in Pugh's mind to do exactly that, but now he decided abruptly that he was going to hang on to the canvasses until he got them to Naples. If he got rid of them at this stage, word would inevitably get back to Tasker, who had his finger in a lot of pies and his ear very close to the ground. If he tried to contact Jones, some officer who would doubtless be an agent for Tasker would be sent to claim them and he'd never see them again – and neither would Tamara. It seemed safer to hide them, and *then* contact Jones.

'I'll leave that for the moment,' Pugh said.

'You ought to report,' the sergeant snapped.

'You do your job, old son,' Pugh snapped back. 'And leave me to do mine.'

The sergeant scowled. 'Well, you'd better get a change of clothes as soon as you can or you'll be arrested. I know your lot. You have officer-type identity documents instead of the ordinary AB64, but they're not endorsed for you to wear civvies.'

'I'm fully aware of that. But I'd have looked a bloody fool behind the German lines, wouldn't I, dressed in a khaki battledress?'

'All right, all right,' the sergeant said sullenly. 'What are you going to do with 'em?'

'My clothes?'

'That lot. The Italians.'

'They go with me to the Commission for the Protection of Arts and Monuments, which, in case you don't know, is a department of the Intelligence Section of the 5th Army, connected with the American Fine Arts and Archives Section, and working in close contact with the Italian Belli Arti e Monumenti.'

'What's that mean?'

'Exactly the same. Arts and Monuments.'

'So why do you need the Italians?'

'To provide the provenance for the pictures.'

'What's provenance?'

'The details that prove they're genuine.'

'Christ,' the sergeant said, 'I'm glad I'm just an ordinary military policeman.'

They were finally clear of the front line and in what ought to have been friendly territory. That it was not entirely friendly soon became obvious from the number of times they were stopped and their presence questioned. The Allied Military Government had arrived, with its officers – town majors, engineers,

157

garrison troops, claims and hirings offices, military police, pay masters, displaced persons units, even the YMCA. Not being fighting troops, they were far less casual than the men whose chief concern was staying alive, and very quick to be officious.

They were also now in the Zona di Camorra, and Pugh was uneasy because they were a long way from the main road and the hills seemed empty of life.

Tamara glanced at him sideways. 'You are worried, Piu,' she said.

'Yes.'

'You expect trouble?'

'This is bandit country. It's dangerous.'

She shrugged. 'Everything is dangerous in Italy.'

However, at last, Pugh's authority was beginning to carry weight. Since the field security people were considered even by a few of the British to be a form of British police, his papers invariably brought a response. Officers and sergeants withdrew their objections to the passage of the hearse, even to the presence of Marco, Foscari, Tassinari and Tamara. And, in the end, an Indian muleteer appeared with a length of rope to put a whipping on the splintered shaft to strengthen it so they could continue.

By this time the weather had improved a little and the sleety rain had stopped, the clouds had cleared, and there was even a suggestion of blue in the sky. A cookhouse had been established in an old warehouse in the main street of the town of Posticci, and the petrol cookers had settled down to a steady glow that could produce 700 breakfasts in just over an hour. The streets were full of dirty-faced weary men just down from the line, their noses twitching at the smell of bacon that hung in the air.

Around them, small Italian boys were touting for their sisters, and in odd empty houses soldiers had started scrubbing the floors, doing their best to get rid of the lice and bedbugs before they started to live in

158

them. Outside the town the ditches were filled with all the rubbish of war – cartridge cases, broken weapons, German helmets – but the shops appeared to be functioning after a fashion, to say nothing of a small, indifferent cinema.

The Via Garibaldi was packed with men in khaki, and there were two restaurants, mostly filled with officers. There was also a false air of gaiety that came from the rapid turnover of money, because the men just down from the line were anxious to spend – on anything, knicknacks, booze, or women, it didn't matter much – and the people of the town, hungry and desperate for money, were only too willing to sell.

Nobody looked twice as the hearse moved among the traffic. Fiorello, the black plumes drooping about his ears after the rain, plopped his great splayed feet down in the mud, his expression one of utter contempt. They were a strange-looking cortège, with three people sitting on the box – Pugh defiantly wearing Ciasca's top hat – and two more sitting in the open rear doors, their feet dangling.

The police sergeant near Bagnano had finally taken pity on their bedraggled state, however, and supplied them with mugs of hot sweet army tea and tins of bully beef, margarine and biscuits, and as they stopped by the roadside to eat, Pugh stretched, feeling they were safe at last.

'Naples tomorrow,' he said, glancing at Tamara. 'And then we'll know how much your pictures are worth.'

'Will you take them to a dealer, Piu?' she asked.

Pugh smiled. 'I'll take one. We'll keep the rest out of sight until I've got an opinion.'

She glanced round at Fiorello chomping on the sweet grass, none the worse for his gallop. 'Won't someone soon want to know what's in the coffin? If they realise how long we've been on the way I think they will be suspicious. A body kept that long would be in a terrible state.'

Soon afterwards, they passed through Cavaltino, the village where the Moroccans had run wild during Pugh's journey north. There were American military police there, in the white helmets and spats that gave them their nickname, Snowdrops. They seemed worried instead of merely hostile and one of them explained why.

'Another bunch of Moroccans came by,' he said. 'Six of the bastards. A different lot altogether, for all we know, but the villagers enticed 'em into one of the houses with promises of booze, food and dames if they'd leave the rest of the village alone. Then they drugged 'em.' The MP shuddered. 'They took 'em up to the bell tower of the church and left 'em to the women because they felt they needed vengeance. They tied 'em up and waited until they recovered consciousness, then they cut the balls off two of 'em and blinded 'em with needles. Then they rang the bells until the bastards went off their heads. We've got 'em in hospital now, blind, deaf and ball-less and half out of their minds, wondering what hit 'em. They'll have the rest of their lives to find the answer. Three of 'em they took out into the fields and left with a live grenade tucked between their legs.'

Pugh stared at the MP with a sick expression. He could never associate the incredible cruelty the Italians sometimes showed with their love of music and children.

'Did you arrest anybody?'

The MP shook his head. 'Who? We know it goddam happened because they telephoned and told us. But you know what it's like round here. Nobody's talking. It's vendetta country and if anybody – even a kid or a dame – opened their mouth, that would be that. Another one would be dead. They said they buried 'em' – the MP pointed at the sloping fields – 'out there somewhere. That's all we can find out. You can hear the sonsabitches laughing and congratulating each other on what a good harvest it'll be, and that's all you can get out of 'em.'

160

'You mentioned five Moroccans. What happened to the other one?'

'He got away. So keep a look-out for him. He's armed and he might be after a bit of vengeance himself.'

By this time the hearse and the coffin were beginning to be an embarrassment. They were stopped again and again and nobody believed Pugh's story, so they were constantly delayed by long arguments and protracted visits to officers for a decision. In the end they decided it was time for a change. The coffin Foscari had made was simply a long oblong box with straight sides with handles attached, so they took off the handles to make it look like a single wardrobe and, finding a man painting the front of his house with watery whitewash, they asked him instead to paint the hearse. He looked bewildered but the money Pugh was offering enabled him to overcome his surprise.

'From now on,' Pugh said, 'this is simply a horse-drawn van.

The painter slapped the whitewash wherever he could, covering the wheels as much as possible and smearing it over the glass panels at the sides and rear of the hearse.

'The horse also, Signore?' he asked nervously.

With the glass daubed over, the hearse looked like a crudely painted baker's cart with unexpected fittings which, they felt, wouldn't arouse a great deal of interest.

At midday they found a small trattoria and, while Pugh went inside with Tamara, Foscari remained outside with Tassinari, watching the horse and making sure Marco didn't run off with the paintings.

The restaurant was in a cellar and was chilly enough for everybody inside to wear their coats, which, it was obvious from a mile away, were all made out of British army blankets. A waiter brought round several fish in a bucket for them to choose from, but they looked like nothing they'd ever seen before and most were in slices so that it was impossible to identify them anyway. They decided to try the veal.

'It's probably mule,' Tamara said.

As they ate, urchins moved through the tables, begging, and they had to keep one hand on their piece of bread so that it wasn't spirited away. Then a small girl in an ordinary chair to which wheels had been attached was pushed in. She had neither hands nor feet and they were told she had lost them in a bomb explosion. As her parents pushed food into her mouth, Tamara had to hurry out, the tears running down her face.

'How much longer do we have to suffer so?' she sobbed.

While they remained with Fiorello, Foscari went into the trattoria with Tassinari and Marco, and when they'd eaten they climbed back to their places and moved southwards out of the town. On the outskirts, the carabinieri stopped them once more and demanded their papers.

'Zona di Camorra,' one of them said, pointing south as he handed the papers back. 'Bandit country. No partisans. Just bandits. They murdered one of our men last week. Caught him on his own and shot him to ribbons.' He paused. 'We gave him a good funeral, though. They're all over. Corneliano Romandi's one of them.'

The Robin Hood of the area had been in prison at the time of the Allied landings but, claiming to be a political prisoner, was released, and had celebrated his freedom by immediately murdering an American soldier for his rifle.

'He thinks Italy should become part of the United States,' the policeman explained, indicating a smudged drawing on a wall showing a crude America and a crude Italy attached by a chain. 'He's planning a coup d'état, they say, to force the Government to do what he wants.'

It wasn't unusual. Half the population of Italy seemed to want to go to America, and Corneliano was gathering his forces round him and arming them with weapons picked up on the battlefields, where there were still plenty for anyone who was interested. He had so many now he was said to be preying on black market operators as they followed the armies northwards, and had hijacked convoys of military supplies, and once even fought a pitched battle with machine guns and grenades with another gang who had had the same idea.

By nightfall they were well into the country again, clinging to the side roads to avoid the military traffic that roared ceaselessly northwards on Highway 6, the main route of the armies in the west. Pugh was frowning, wondering if he'd told the police sergeant near Bagnano too much. He'd probably make a report which would be seen by his officer and passed down the line through the usual channels, eventually to reach Tasker. On the other hands, the sergeant hadn't seemed very bright, and knew nothing about art, so the name Detto Banti probably wouldn't stick in his mind and, if it did, he probably wouldn't do much about it.

They had removed another picture from the coffin – this time one of a man fondling a girl through an open doorway, called *The Stolen Embrace*. It was in the best style of the English story-telling Victorian artists.

'He has his hand on her breast,' Tamara said bluntly. 'And she has a look in her eye that suggests she is encouraging him. It is obscene.'

'Perhaps that's a good reason to have it handy,' Pugh decided. 'Anybody demanding a bribe will jump at it.'

Excluding the three small framed paintings, they were now down to nine canvasses and had reached the better ones lower down so that it was becoming difficult to decide which, if necessary, to offer next.

That night they slept in a barn belonging to a farmer, Tamara being given a bed in the house. The farmer's wife obviously suspected her husband's intentions because he had the same look in his eye as the man in *The Stolen Embrace* and, sure enough, just as Pugh was settling down to sleep in the barn, wrapped in the velvet curtain, he found Tamara standing by his side.

'He tried to get into bed with me,' she announced. 'I think it is safer to sleep with you, Piu.'

He moved over and offered half the curtain and she lay down in the straw, her back to him.

'I think there will be many insects in the straw,' she said.

'Scots Greys,' Pugh said.

She lifted her head.

'That's what soldiers call them. They say they carry out manoeuvres up and down their chests.'

She seemed to find it funny. She sat up and looked at Pugh. 'I think you are a good man, Piu,' she said. 'Many times now I have slept alongside you and you have always been the perfect gentleman.'

'You ought to see me shaved and with my hair cut.'

It was a standard army reply and she didn't understand it. 'I think you would be well behaved even with your hair cut. I think you are a man of high principles.'

'Wait till we get to Naples. It'll be different then. It'll be an all-in, knock-down, drag-out affair and you'll have to take your chances.'

'Che?'

He explained. 'If I meet you in Naples I shan't be responsible for your safety. I shall be an ordinary soldier full of an ordinary soldier's lusts.'

'You are going to see me when we get to Naples?'

'Any objection?'

'I think I would be pleased. I have a small apartment. Two rooms and a kitchen. It will be enough, I think.'

'Enough for what?'

She looked at him with a frown, then the old grin broke through. 'I think, Piu,' she said, 'that we had better go to sleep.'

2

The following morning, they pushed off early. The farmer's wife was obviously glad to see the back of them, and the farmer, who had probably had a bad night with her, remained in the background, glowering.

At lunchtime, they stopped beside the road and made a fire and, finding water in a stream running down from the hills, prepared to make coffee. The sun was warm for a change and they sat around enjoying the drink, the Italians rolling their eyes at the quality after the acorn coffee they'd been drinking for years.

As they talked, they decided to choose the best of the remaining paintings for offer to a reliable dealer, so Foscari removed the lid of the coffin and they took out the canvasses, unrolled them and propped them up among the rocks round the fire.

'Nine,' Pugh said. He looked at Tamara. 'Not as many as we set off with.'

She shrugged. 'Italy is full of disasters.'

They discussed the paintings for a while, huddled round the rear end of the hearse.

'*The Stolen Embrace* is better than the sheeps' backsides,' Tassinari said. 'But it is still not what I would call a good Detto Banti. The green of the man's trousers is right, of course, but there's something about the way he's standing that seems to miss Bocco's exactness of line. What are we planning to do with the rest of them?'

'We're going to hide them,' Pugh said. 'And offer one only, until I've had time to check on just who's interested. It might bring a few surprises.'

Tassinari didn't object. 'Which one?'

They began to discuss the relative qualities of the remaining paintings. Pugh stared at *Washerwomen at a Stream*, frowning.

'The one on the left looks as if she has a wooden leg,' he said.

Marco glared at him. 'She looks all right to me,' he growled.

'The self-portrait would be condemned straight away,' Tassinari observed. 'It was copied from the photograph. He's just changed the clothing and the hat. You'll notice that the hat's small so there need be no shadow on the face.' He gestured. '*The March on Rome*. I wonder if Mussolini ever saw that.'

'Perhaps he did,' Pugh said. 'And when he did, he didn't like it. Which is why it ended up in the cellar.'

'*Three Sisters*.' Tassinari stared shrewdly. 'There is much fraud about these paintings, Sergeant. As though Bocco dashed them off in a hurry.'

'He did sometimes,' Marco growled. 'Between bottles.'

'As if he were using the tricks but not a lot of skill.'

'He was getting old and his skill was fading.'

Pugh turned to Tamara. 'Which do *you* think is best?'

'I like the *Still Life with Chessmen*.'

'A good choice,' Marco said.

Tassinari nodded. 'I think so, too,' he agreed. 'It's not Bocco's style or even his usual choice of subject but he seems to have taken time over that one.' He glanced at Marco. 'Perhaps at that time he wasn't drinking.'

Marco shrugged. 'He had periods when he didn't touch it.'

'We'll make it the still life then,' Pugh said. 'But it's still only the best of a poor lot and probably not even genuine. It's a good job we also have the three small ones Enrichetta tried to steal.'

He fished them from the coffin and propped them against the wheel of the hearse. 'These are first-rate Detto Bantis,' he said. 'The way he painted when he was

166

young.' He gestured at the one on the left. 'That's a reunion. In good rousing style. One of his best, with the green very prominent. The others are pictures of soldiers and gypsies, which he always enjoyed. Both solid nineteenth-century paintings. Better than *Garibaldi and Vittorio Emmanuelo* and more stylish than any of the others.'

'They're not very big,' Marco complained.

'Size isn't value,' Pugh said. 'But it's the larger ones that are the problem so I think it should perhaps be one of those. We'll stick to the still life.'

They were just about to rise when a noise in the bushes near them whipped their heads round. Immediately they were all on their feet.

Pugh stared about him, in his mind the thought of the solitary *goumier* who had escaped the harsh ministrations of the village of Cavaltino.

'Stay here,' he said to Marco. 'Keep your eyes open.'

Pushing into the bushes with Foscari, he hadn't gone more than twenty yards when he heard a yell from where they had been sitting. Foscari, who was just ahead of him crashing through the bushes, didn't appear to have heard, so Pugh turned at once and headed back. Snatching up a broken branch, as he emerged from the trees he caught sight of Tassinari stretched on the ground unconscious and Marco reeling away and falling. Then he heard Tamara give a shuddering sound that was half a scream and half a cry of alarm, and saw a figure which had been crouching over Marco rise to its feet. It was a man in a grey woollen cloak-type garment striped thinly with brown. His black eyes glittered and his nose was curved like a scimitar.

One thin brown hand stretched out and grasped Tamara's wrist and the other wrenched at her dress. As it tore, Pugh yelled and the Moroccan turned, his face twisted into a grin made tigerish by the thin moustache that curved round his mouth. He was just reaching for his rifle, which he had rested against the wheel of the hearse, when Pugh hit him with the branch. It caught him at the side of the head so that he seemed to be lifted off his feet. One of his booted feet caught the picture of the washerwomen and sent it whirling away, then he fell back, half under the hearse. The noise had startled Fiorello and he jerked nervously and tugged at his tethering rope. Pugh snatched up the rifle and flung it away as far as he could before reaching for Tamara. She flung herself at him and he held her in his arms, but it was Tamara who pushed herself free.

'Oh, Piu,' she cried. 'Look!'

Whirling round, expecting to see the *goumier* coming at them with a knife, he saw what had caused her distress. The picture of the washerwomen had fallen face upwards on to the fire, and already there was a brown spreading scorch mark in the middle of it, almost obliterating the figures as the paint bubbled and ran.

As he snatched it from the flames, Foscari reappeared. Then Pugh realised that the Moroccan had vanished from under the hearse and, as Foscari gestured, he saw a figure bolting across the fields, almost like something out of a ghost story, thin and ungainly with its long legs and huge boots, the brown-grey cloak flapping as it ran.

Marco was sitting up now, holding his head, and Tamara, trying to hold her dress together, was staring at the *Washerwomen*. As she dropped to her knees, Pugh saw that she was weeping.

'I'm sorry, Tamara,' he said. 'But there are still eight others.'

She looked up. '*Caro* Piu,' she said softly. 'It isn't the painting I'm weeping for. It's for me. My past. These paintings are all I had of my family. There's nothing else. Nothing at all. I never knew it, and now it's dwindled just a little more.'

They stopped at midday to eat the sausage and bread they had bought from the farmer the night before and to drink a bottle of wine as acrid as vinegar. Tamara was

168

still a little shaken after the attack by the *goumier* and seemed low in spirits. She had managed to make repairs to the neck of her dress but, Pugh noticed, she never left his side, as if he were the only one she felt she could trust.

As there was grazing for Fiorello, they took him out of the shafts and tethered him to a tree so he could bury his nose in the grass. When they backed him into the shafts again, he held his head up for at least five minutes before allowing it to sink.

'I think he is feeling better,' Foscari said. 'He looks almost as if he might be alive.'

They set off again, the old horse plodding slowly round the slopes of the hills. As they approached a wood spread on either side of the road, a man stepped out. He looked like a farm labourer and Pugh yanked at the reins, thinking he was looking for a lift. But as Fiorello clopped to a halt, a revolver as big as an anti-aircraft gun appeared, pointed directly at Pugh's head.

'Oh, God, no!' Pugh said, wondering if they would never be free of villainy.

'*Mani in alto!*'

As Pugh lifted his arms, more men appeared from the trees. They were all armed, some with rifles, some with revolvers, two or three even with tommy guns. From among them a tall, burly man stepped forward. He had a neck like a bull, broad shoulders and crinkly black hair. His smile was wide.

He began to walk round the hearse, studying it, staring at the chrome lampholders, cherubs, skulls and wreaths. Tapping the glass and peering closer, he scratched at the whitewashed side with his fingernail until the black varnished paint showed through.

'This is a hearse,' he said.

Pugh admitted the fact.

The burly man's eyes narrowed. 'Who are you?' he demanded.

It was Tassinari who answered. 'We are the family of

169

Arturo Fornaciari,' he said, without batting an eyelid.
'Who's he?'

'Nobody special.' The old man was becoming an expert liar. 'He died in Moccino and we are taking him to Caserta to bury him alongside his son. The Germans were shelling the cemetery where his wife lies.'

The young man's eyes narrowed shrewdly. 'Did this Arturo Fornaciari have money?' he asked.

'No,' Tassinari said. 'He had once, but he spent it all.'

The man drew himself up. 'You know who I am?' he asked. 'I am Corneliano.'

Pugh had suspected as much from the start, though he was surprised to see how unlike the descriptions he was. He was by no means young and had a twisted nose, a wide mouth and straggly hair. It seemed to be an indication of the Italian wish for romance. They wanted to see their local bandit as a handsome romantic figure and so the stories had grown, and the rumours of his gallantry probably didn't match the truth either.

Corneliano took off his hat, and stood with it across his chest as he gestured with his tommy gun. 'That hearse looks as if it might be valuable,' he said.

'If you take the hearse, Signor Corneliano,' Tassinari pointed out, 'how do we get Arturo Fornaciari to Caserta? How do we bury him alongside his son, who died in 1941, a victim of the Fascists?'

Corneliano's smile disappeared. 'I sympathise with you, old man,' he said. 'You can keep the hearse. What about the horse?'

'Fiorello's no good for anything but horsemeat. He'll probably drop dead before we reach Caserta, anyway. But it would be nice if he got us so near we didn't have to carry the coffin too far.'

Corneliano considered for a moment. 'There must be money,' he said.

'No, Signor Corneliano. No money.'

'I think you are not telling the truth, old man. Why otherwise does Arturo Fornaciari have so many mourners? Poor men in Italy these days find it difficult to attract mourners. Mourning is an expensive business, and here we have five mourners. Why are *five* mourners all so anxious to see Arturo Fornaciari safely buried?' By this time he had opened the doors at the back of the hearse and was peering inside. 'What is that inside?'

'The coffin, signore, containing Arturo Fornaciari.'

'You are not giving Arturo Fornaciari a very good funeral, old man. This is no more than a cheap box.'

Tassinari shrugged. 'All we could afford.'

'You have curtains in there?'

'Very dirty curtains, Signor Corneliano. They were all that were worth taking from Arturo Fornaciari's house.'

Pugh was holding his breath, praying the bandit wouldn't explore any further because underneath the curtains was the lascivious gentleman and his naughty girl friend of *The Stolen Embrace*.

'The fittings look as if they might be valuable,' Corneliano said. 'I think we'll take them. They'll fetch a good price.'

The crucifix that wouldn't stay upright was wrenched off. The screws came out of the ancient woodwork without effort, so Corneliano's men began to wrench at the lampholders and the other chrome fittings. When they'd finished, the old hearse looked more dilapidated than ever.

Corneliano was looking thoughtful. 'Rings?' he asked.

Tassinari took out his watch chain – which had always been minus a watch – and offered it. Pugh handed over his wrist watch, Tamara a necklace. Corneliano looked at Foscari.

'You?'

'He's an escaped British prisoner of war we picked up,' Pugh said quickly in case they tried to force him to join them. 'He is trying to reach the British army. He has nothing. He had nothing when he first appeared. The poor of Italy helped him this far.'

The bandit leader patted Foscari's shoulder. 'Good luck, my friend,' he said. 'See that you destroy the *tedeschi.*' He looked at Marco. 'And you? We have had nothing from you yet?'

'I haven't got anything.'

'What about a wedding ring?'

'I'm not married. I've never married. I've never been able to afford being married.'

Corneliano scowled and began to clean his fingernails with a knife. 'I don't believe you, my friend,' he said. 'Perhaps you need persuading to tell the truth. You have the look of a man who has money.'

He gestured and two of his men grabbed Marco's arms. 'Perhaps we will start by breaking a few fingers.'

'No, no!'

Tamara turned towards Pugh, who put his arm round her.

'On the other hand, perhaps it might be better to cut off an ear first.'

'No!' Marco's voice had risen to a shriek. 'The painting!'

Corneliano lowered the knife. 'Painting?' he said. 'What painting?'

Tassinari interrupted. 'There is a painting in the hearse,' he said quietly. 'It has no value, but you might be able to sell it.'

'Get it.'

Pugh climbed into the hearse and produced *The Stolen Embrace* from under the old curtains. Losing pictures seemed to be part of the game now but, like Tassinari, he was growing more and more suspicious about the Detto Banti canvasses and was determined not to risk anyone's life for them.

Corneliano held the canvas at arm's length and stared at it, then he handed it to two of his men and gestured. They moved away so he could study it at a distance.

'I think it is a good painting,' he said. 'I don't know

much about painting but it looks good to me.'

'It's a Detto Banti,' Marco shrieked.

'What is a Detto Banti?'

Tassinari explained. 'Detto Banti was a painter of some renown,' he said.

'Like Tintoretto and Titian? Like Longhi and Lotto and Canaletto?'

'Something like that,' Tassinari agreed. 'But *they* were great painters. Detto Banti was not a great painter.' He shrugged. 'Though he painted some good things and some of his works have value.'

'And this one?'

Tassinari shrugged again. 'It has his signature on it.' He pointed to the scarlet scrawl. 'That's it, but he had students and they copied his work. He even signed some of them and sold them as his own. He was a greedy man and not very honest.'

Corneliano's eyebrows lifted. 'This is what artists do?'

'Some of them do it a lot.'

'And this is one?'

'This one belonged to Arturo Fornaciari. He obtained it years ago in payment of some debt. I don't know where it came from or whether it is genuine or not.'

Corneliano grinned. 'I think we shall be able to persuade *someone* it is genuine,' he said. 'How much is it worth?'

Tassinari shrugged. 'If it's genuine, perhaps a million lire!'

'*È vero?* As much as that?'

'Perhaps more. If it's not genuine, two or three thousand. No more.'

Corneliano's smile came again. 'I think it will *become* genuine,' he said. 'We will make sure it becomes genuine. I will take advice from experts. Will people question it?'

'They might ask for the provenance.'

'What is that?'

Tassinari explained. 'However,' he admitted, 'I've no

173

doubt you could produce some. A man of your ability and intelligence should be able to find a dealer who, for a small fee, would produce what you want. That would convince a buyer.'

'I think it would.' Corneliano rolled the painting again and pointed at the hearse. 'I think you had better go now, family of Arturo Fornaciari. Before I change my mind and take the horse and the hearse, and even the coffin.'

They climbed back to their places and Pugh jerked the reins. Fiorello leaned against the harness and the hearse moved slowly away. As it passed him, Corneliano waved the rolled painting.

'A good day's work, my friends, I think,' he said.

3

'Don't ever complain again about giving pictures away,' Pugh snarled.

Marco scowled. 'He'd have cut my ear off,' he said.

Pugh had to admit that there had been that possibility, but it was useful to have a lever to halt Marco's constant complaining about what was happening to the pictures. 'You've got a spare,' he said. 'At the other side of your head.' He frowned. 'I'm beginning to think that if we get half a dozen of the paintings to Naples, we can count ourselves lucky.'

'We haven't tried hard enough,' Marco said.

'How else would we have done it?'

Tamara spoke from alongside Pugh. 'Considering we started on the wrong side of the line, have been halted by rapacious Germans, partisans and gangsters, we have been lucky to lose only four.'

'Five,' Marco growled. 'You gave one to the nuns.'

'Which I do not regret. And since they are supposed to be mine, I think I should be the one to complain. We still have seven – worth about 28 million lire – and that is a fortune to anyone.'

'Together with three small ones,' Pugh reminded her, 'which might well be more valuable than all the others put together.'

'Also the family silver which Enrichetta was about to remove and didn't. Fortunately, Corneliano didn't think of that.'

They reached Origono by darkness. It was a quiet town, built on the side of a wooded hill and far enough from the war to have recovered some of its poise. They could hear music, African in manner, not the sweet Neapolitan melodies, as they halted in the square under the inevitable statue of Garibaldi. The *questura*, the police station, stood opposite them and, after a long discussion, they decided to inform the police what had happened.

'They will want to know about the *marocchino*,' Tamara said. 'He must not terrify any more women. And they will doubtless be pleased to know that Corneliano Romandi is not far away.'

'They may even recover the painting,' Tassinari added.

Unfortunately, they had arrived at just the wrong moment because the *questura* was bubbling with excitement at the news, which had just arrived, that the Allies had finally burst through the line at Cassino and were racing towards Rome. Chief of Police Renza, a fat man with eyes like a spaniel, was sitting at a desk, sweating in front of a fan that was directed on to his body, and had to be bullied to listen to what they had to say. When he finally dragged his attention from the radio, however, he was all ears. The news about the breakthrough had interrupted a consultation about dealing with the bandits in the area, so there were delighted smiles all round at the news of Corneliano.

'This is good,' Renza said. 'We thought he was near here, but we have been waiting to be certain. We shall now catch him. We know there's a black market convoy of tyres due to move north to Rome as soon as it's freed. Now that the Germans have pulled back and the Americans are moving forward, the black market is moving with it. Corneliano knows that as well as we do and will try to stop it.' He paused and examined his nails, his expression thoughtful. 'This painting you mention that was stolen, Signor Sergente,' he went on slowly. 'Is it valuable?'

'It's a Detto Banti.'

Renza had clearly never heard of Bocco Detto Banti,

but he put on a good performance of pretending he had. 'I see. And its value, Signor Sergente?'

'Over a million lire. The Italian Government is interested in it. As also is the British Government and the American Government.'

'A prize worth having, I think.'

'Yes.'

Renza nodded slowly. 'We'll get your painting and the fittings from your hearse back for you, Sergente. It so happens that we have learned that Corneliano has a woman in Spazzi and he's visiting her tonight. We intend to be outside Spazzi, in two detachments, a hundred yards apart so that we shall be certain to trap him. Perhaps the Signore Sergente would like to be present.' Renza's smile became encouraging, then suddenly it slid away and was replaced by a puzzled frown. 'Incidentally,' he ended, 'why is the Signore Sergente travelling in a hearse?'

The found a small albergo, where they took rooms for the night. It was bare and spartan but there was a small stone-floored restaurant alongside where they could guarantee a meal. 'Nothing special, Signori,' the proprietor explained. 'These days, there is never anything special in Italy. But it *is* a meal. Perhaps cabbage soup. With' – he shrugged, obviously considering Pugh a sympathetic listener – 'perhaps a little tinned beef. You understand?' He placed his finger alongside his nose. 'One doesn't question where it comes from.'

Foscari decided he was going to accompany Pugh on Renza's ambush, and as they left the restaurant they hitched at their belts and pulled their clothes more tightly round them.

Tamara was worried. 'Will there be guns?' she asked.

'I suspect so.'

'You will not get shot, Piu?'

He grinned. 'I'll try not to.'

'I should not like you to be shot.'

'It's not something I'm keen on myself.'

Pugh and Foscari watched as the carabinieri and the pubblica sicurezza groups gathered at the police station. They all had obsolete weapons and there were a lot of jokes about dying, but they climbed into cars and began to drive out of the town along the straight road that led northward, parallel with the road the armies were using. Because the armies didn't frequent this route, it was regularly used by black marketeers, swindlers, gangsters and crooks.

Spazzi was typical of the villages on the slopes of the hills behind Naples. It was crooked, with twisting streets and knuckled alleys, its brown-tiled roofs hiding pink-, green- and blue-washed houses. Most of the life of the place went on in the streets, in the flare of the welcome warming sun. Black-garbed women were washing and feeding their children and preparing the meals on the pavement, watched by lean dogs and groups of aimless men leaning against the walls, their hands in their pockets.

They waited before they moved, then they stopped close to a band shadowed by a grove of trees. Rain had not fallen for some time and the day's heat had turned the recent mud to dust. The policemen took up positions on either side of the road that ran alongside the town and pushed out a light two-wheeled cart they borrowed from a neighbouring farm to make a road block.

The first car to appear was powered by gas and was full of people, all of whom had papers that were blatantly false. It was stacked with contraband – American cigarettes, nylons, torch batteries, tins of bully beef, packets of K rations, needles, cloth, nails, watches, spectacle frames; all articles in short supply which would fetch a good price on the black market. Curiously it also contained coffin handles from which, with a sheepish look at Pugh, Foscari helped himself. 'If they can,' he said, 'I think *we* can, Signor Sergente.'

Renza was very stern and upright, despite the

pleadings, the offers of bribes, the whispered promises. He didn't show much interest in the contents of the car but prowled round it, staring at the tyres.

'These are British Dunlops,' he announced. 'Army issue.'

'No,' the owner of the car said. 'Italian Pirellis. I got them from my brother. See, the name's there.'

Renza was not impressed. 'The British markings have been burned off with electricity,' he said, 'and these stamped on afterwards. The tyres must be removed.'

There was a wail of protest but he was adamant, and immediately there was a hurried consultation, more whispering, more bribes. Renza was like a rock, and the police jacked up the rear of the car.

'How do we get home?' the driver asked in despair.

'On the rims.'

'It will ruin the wheels.'

'Then you must buy new ones.'

'There aren't any to be had.'

Renza shrugged. 'Then I fear you will have to stop driving. Be satisfied. You have not been arrested. Your car's full of contraband but I intend to take only the tyres.'

The car drove off, rattling and clattering on empty rims and, as the confiscated tyres were rolled to the police lorry, Foscari looked sad and shocked.

'They'll end up in the same place,' Pugh said grimly. 'On the black market. The police aren't very well paid.'

By this time they had stopped several other cars. All those with a bribe to offer were allowed to pass. Those who argued had their goods confiscated. At the end of two hours with no sign of Corneliano it was beginning to look as if the information they'd received about him was wrong, but then, suddenly, a lorry appeared on the horizon.

'Eh!' one of the policemen shouted. 'What's this?'

'It's Corneliano!'

Moving behind the cart, the policemen clicked off the

safety catches of their weapons. The lorry, which was travelling at speed, was driven by a man who could well have been the *goumier* who had attacked Tamara, his brown face half hidden by a woollen hat. The police headlights had half blinded him but he made no attempt to stop and, as the police opened fire, the lorry slewed across the road, its windscreen smashed, dropped a wheel in the ditch, leapt into the air and performed a spectacular somersault. As it hit the ground and burst into flames, the policemen started running.

When they reached the lorry, the driver was lying alongside, with what looked like a broken neck, and another man, trapped in the cabin, was screaming vainly for help. A lot of black market tyres had burst out of the back. While the police were trying to drag things clear to get at the trapped man, a second lorry came roaring out of the darkness and they all had to run for safety. The new arrival burst through the flames and smoke and, followed by shots from the policemen, smashed into the cart. It was like an explosion, with planks, shafts and pieces of wood flying in all directions, then, as the cart collapsed in splinters, the two wheels rolling away, the lorry vanished into the night, the engine missing badly as though the collision had done some damage. As they recovered their breath, they realised that the man in the burning lorry was dead.

Everybody began to argue about whose fault it was, but Renza reassured them. 'Have no fear,' he said. 'I know where they will have gone. Since we haven't got Corneliano and don't look like getting him, we'll pick them up instead.'

Leaving two men behind to guard the wreckage, he directed the rest back to their vehicles and they headed after the vanished lorry. After a while they turned off the road and ground their way along a stony, uneven track to where they could see a large low-slung building against the night sky. There was a barn-like structure alongside, with farm implements leaning against the walls, among them an ancient wooden plough. Two oxen placidly eyed the police vehicles as they approached.

Renza stopped them well away from the house and they advanced on foot, all keeping their heads down in case a blast of fire came from the group of shabby buildings. They found the lorry that had escaped, marked by bullet holes, hidden behind the barn and still loaded with tyres and spare parts.

Renza nodded and gestured, and his men headed for the house. To their surprise they heard music, and as they burst in they found themselves facing a roomful of men and women dancing to a mandolin and a piano-accordion. As the police appeared, the dancing stopped. Renza stared at the couples, his eyes searching the faces. There was no sign of Corneliano.

'Who are all these people?'

'Guests,' one of the women said. 'There has been a christening. They came for the celebrations.'

'In a lorry full of black market tyres? Where is the baby?'

'Its mother took it home. It was badly in need of feeding.'

One of the policemen, searching the other rooms, reappeared, pushing before him a man whose shirt was soaked with blood. The woman who had first spoken shrugged. 'You know what it's like,' she said. 'Get half a dozen men together and a couple of bottles of wine, and there's bound to be a fight. Somebody says something and out comes a knife.'

The police lined everybody up along the wall. One of the men turned out to be a deserter from the American army, another a weasel-like little man with a Liverpool accent who had gone missing as soon as he set foot ashore at Salerno and had been living on his wits ever since. There was a lot of loot, too, but Pugh had a feeling that very little would find its way to the *amasso*, the government pool where retrieved stolen goods were stored. And there wouldn't be any tyres among it, he felt sure.

'There are only four of them,' the police sergeant said, as the captives were led away.

'We'll get no promotion with four,' Renza said, nodding to his men. 'We need more. Go into the village. Pick up a few more. Make sure they've got records. It won't be difficult. Everybody has a record these days.'

As they pushed the men into the police vehicles, Pugh watched expressionlessly. The men they had picked up had accepted with resignation the charges against them, though they had been nowhere near the ambush. It was the way things were done and promotion gained.

Back in Origono, Police Chief Renza was disappointed that Corneliano had not turned up but was optimistic that they would have another chance. Later Pugh was called to the *questura*.

'Have no fear, Sergente,' Renza said. 'We'll find your painting. Our information was wrong. It wasn't Spazzi where Corneliano went. It was Sili, across the valley, and it's not a woman, it's cards. Corneliano likes gambling and, what is more, he likes winning – so he cheats. We know he'll be in Sili tonight. Aldo Galo told us. He lost a lot of money to him a week or two ago and he wants his own back. He says there are drugs in the house. He says your painting's there, too.'

Tamara was unhappy about what was going on. 'I would rather they kept the painting,' she said, 'than have you in danger, Piu.'

'No danger to me,' Pugh pointed out. 'I'll be keeping my head down. But the painting's there and I've got to be around to identify it. There might be a whole houseful of paintings.'

It took a day or two to lay on the raid because Renza had to call up the pubblica sicurezza again for extra men, while the Canadian army, which was running the area, offered to supply a few more. But on the day they had decided to make the raid, they heard the Allies were on the point of entering Rome and as they clung to the radio, listening to the BBC's broadcasts, no one would listen to Pugh's protests. In the end, the raid was postponed and the following day they learned that the Americans had entered the capital. Renza was delighted.

'Tonight!' he said. 'Tonight we will do it! They will have been celebrating the liberation of the Città Eterna. They will be drunk and unable to resist.'

The same procedure was gone through, the same minute attention to detail, as if the policemen suspected Corneliano was too clever for them. In the evening they gathered as before, with their ancient weapons and the same jokes about dying, then at midnight, they climbed into cars and lorries and drove round the valley to the town of Sili situated on the slopes at the other side. It turned out to be a replica of Spazzi, with the same crooked alleys and steep streets. Because the grind of gears might alert their quarry, they stopped the vehicles at the bottom of the hill and climbed out. Nobody spoke and Renza gave his orders by signs.

Two or three policemen from the local station appeared and led them via the back streets to a square in the centre of the town. They moved silently, keeping close to the walls and making the most of the shadows. Eventually, they stopped outside a square house standing alone, separate from the rest, surrounded by a narrow strip of land.

'The house of Galo,' one of the local policemen said. 'That's where he is. We saw him go in. He's not come out yet.'

Renza ordered half his men to the back of the house. Gesturing imperiously, he instructed the remainder to fan out so that all four sides of the house were covered. For a long time, they waited, whispering urgently, then finally, just when Pugh was beginning to wonder what was holding up the operation, he saw Renza lift his revolver.

The crash of the shot echoed round the village. At once shutters were flung open on all sides of the square and almost immediately they heard the thunder of a volley from the back of the house. There was no other movement and the shutters were immediately slammed to again. For a long time there was silence, then a policeman appeared through the darkness, keeping to the shadows as if he expected retaliatory fire from somewhere.

'We've got him,' he announced. 'He got on the roof through a window at the back. He's in the courtyard.'

They moved warily to the back of the building. In the courtyard a man lay across the wreckage of an old barrow, relaxed as though asleep. He was half on his side, face downwards, one knee drawn up, one arm flung out. On his hip was a pistol holster, but it was empty, and close to his right hand was a Beretta submachine gun. A puddle of blood lay beneath his head.

Renza looked at Pugh. 'This is Corneliano?'

Pugh nodded. 'That's him.'

'You can swear to this?'

'His clothes are the same. His face is that of the man who stopped us.'

Renza laid a hand on Pugh's arm. 'Wait here,' he said. 'We must investigate the house. There may be members of the gang inside. You had better keep your head down.'

Returning to the shadows, Pugh waited. For a long time there was silence but no more shooting. After a while one of the police cars appeared and went round the back of the house. Two minutes later it drove off into the darkness at speed, then men appeared carrying suitcases. One of them handed Pugh a bag containing the chrome lampholders and the decorative wreaths, cherubs, skulls and leaves from Ciasca's old hearse.

'Yours, I think,' he said.

184

Eventually, Renza appeared. With him he had a man. He was small and looked frightened. Renza gestured to his men and they took the man away to a car.

'Is that Galo?'

'That's him.'

'What'll happen to him?'

'He'll die, of course.'

'Who'll kill him?'

Renza shrugged. 'Corneliano's family. They'll get him. There'll be no mark on him but he'll be dead. A hat-pin through the ear to the brain. A sharpened rod up the backside to the stomach. The human body has several useful orifices.' He indicated the man with the suitcase. 'We found the drugs.'

Pugh drew a deep breath. 'And the painting?' he asked.

Renza shrugged, his face expressionless. 'There was no sign of the painting,' he said. 'It seems to have disappeared.'

4

'The police took it, didn't they?' Tamara said.

'Yes,' Pugh agreed. 'They took it.'

'They are very poorly paid, of course,' she said slowly.
She didn't seem to mind as much as he'd expected.
'There are still 28 million lire-worth of canvasses,' she
said. 'And I'm glad they captured the bandit.'

'They didn't capture him,' Pugh said. 'They shot him.'

By daylight, Sili was packed with newspapermen, not
only Italians from Naples but Americans and British
from Rome. Naples was now old hat and they had
milked the capture of Rome to the limit, so the death of
someone like Corneliano, who had often featured in
their stories for his boldness, gave them something
extra. The British, who in England had four small pages
as big as a pocket handkerchief to fill, weren't too
concerned with the case because it had to compete with
the home news and the news from other theatres of
war, but the Americans with their massive journals had
plenty of room. Corneliano had been in the news for
some time, and they were linking him to the growing
anarchy in Italy. Their stories sounded almost as if
they'd been lifted from *La Nazione*, the black news
magazine the Italians loved to read, with its stories of
shattered bodies, air crashes, sinking ships and murders.

They were filing all sorts of items: it was a case of
laying one's money and taking one's choice. None of the
stories matched and the facts were largely guesswork or
imagination. The hotels were packed and the telephones
had a waiting list hours long, while the streets were
overflowing with uniforms – not only Italian police

uniforms, but also the uniforms of British and American security and supply officers, there to identify the loot that had been found.

Police Chief Renza's face appeared in the Italian papers, his head well up so that his double chin didn't show. He manifested no further interest in the painting that had disappeared and in the end they decided it wasn't worth waiting for, because it was clear it would never turn up.

They set off early, two days after the shooting, as soon as Renza had made out his reports and filed their complaints and their description of the missing canvas. He was full of sad smiles but was far from helpful. They were glad to head for Naples, and Foscari's soaring spirits caused him to break into song. Before long they were all singing with him.

As they entered the city, Pugh saw a hearse approaching him and realised he was becoming very familiar with hearses. He recognised this one as belonging to Cirri, the man who liked to take a drink at the O Sole Mio bar, and wondered what he was doing so far out of the city. But there was a coffin in the back, so he decided he must be going to collect a corpse. Perhaps he was well known and his custom extensive.

Tamara studied the hearse as it passed and watched sombrely as an old farm truck, driven on black market petrol but without tyres, clattered over the rutted road, the farmer and his family heading for the fields, then she touched Pugh's arm.

'I shall be glad to be back, Piu,' she said. 'It is time I returned to work. There will be a lot of explaining to do, I think. "Where have you been? What have you been doing?"' She smiled, 'I will tell them I have become an heiress and a wealthy woman. Perhaps they will be pleased for me.'

Naples hadn't changed much and people were still waiting with their usual incredible patience for the crowded trolley buses. But there was also an air of pleasure at the news about Rome and that the Germans, unspeakably tired and dirty, were withdrawing to a new line further north. Rejected and ignored by the wealthy northerners, who had always treated them as inferiors, the Neapolitans found a measure of quiet satisfaction that it was now the northerners' turn to suffer.

It had become warm suddenly and the sky was dull and low, a hot dank grey, the lifeless air beneath it stirred only by occasional wafts of sultry wind that lifted the dust and grit from the gutters. The sea was like a leaden lake, and in the narrow streets where the festoons of washing hung listlessly, the clogged and pullulating city endured its flies and dust, the children swirling in games of football, the babies fretful in the heat, the torn posters fluttering and the smell of excrement and blocked urinals filling the air.

With its blotched housefronts of worn and leprous stucco, the city looked a little like a raddled old whore who'd seen better days. The buildings looked more dilapidated, the people more shabby. If anything, there was less food in the shops, less work and less money, but the streets were still filled with Americans and British, well-fed, well-clothed, and self-confident with the arrogance of victors. Naples was the place in Italy where the sights, sounds and smells were strongest and where the people wore their emotions on their sleeves, their lives an expression of laughter, tears, gaiety and sadness, a million of the best actors in the world putting on an eternally unfolding play in which the comedy was broad and the tragedy violent, and on which the curtain never came down because the Neapolitans clung with an undespairing tenacity to life, courageous and always naïvely impressed by material grandeur, but never impervious to the human spirit.

It had been Pugh's intention to leave the hearse in Caserta but, by the time they reached it, he had decided to take it all the way. The old horse had done wonders. Having drawn them a distance of nearly a hundred miles from Vicinamontane, somehow the old beast seemed to have the right to take them the full distance. He knew Mori, the old carter, would hide the hearse and give the old horse shelter.

He dropped Tamara at the apartment block where she occupied her three small rooms. Inevitably, the elevator wasn't working. Inside her apartment he handed her a duffel bag he'd picked up from the Americans in Cavaltino.

'What is it?'

'Your clothes.'

She looked quickly at him, tested the weight of the bag and looked at him again. 'They are very heavy clothes.'

'Very heavy,' he agreed quietly. 'Three framed paintings signed by Bocco Detto Banti. I put them there in Origono, while the military police were questioning everybody about the *goumier*.'

Her crooked grin came and she held the duffel bag under her coat.

'Have you somewhere you can put them with safety?'

She paused. 'There is a place.'

'Hide them. And don't mention them to anybody.'

Tassinari lived in one large room of a decaying palace in the Via Sipolari, into which every scrap of furniture he possessed had been crammed. It smelled of damp and dry rot, but Tassinari's manners didn't slip and he offered coffee and brandy. It seemed doubtful if he could afford to dispense either, but Pugh knew he would be mortally offended if he refused them.

As he left, Tassinari offered him a card with his name on it and Pugh was startled to see the old lawyer had a title.

Tassinari gestured indifferently. 'Titles mean nothing,' he said. 'After all, when the war is over, we might all be Communists. We will talk about the paintings when you come. By then you will have found out things. I trust you, Sergeant.'

'And I you, Avvocato.'

'Will you see the Signorina Tamara again?'

Pugh nodded and the old man laid a hand on his arm. 'It is good for young men to pick roses in June, because memories are necessary when it comes to December.'

They removed the *Still Life with Chessmen* from the coffin and, as Pugh rolled it up carefully and wrapped it in a piece of old newspaper Tassinari provided, Foscari screwed the coffin lid down again.

Tassinari had agreed to provide a bed for Marco until he could find something, and Pugh and Foscari drove the whitewashed hearse round to old Mori in the Via Villari. He was outside when they arrived, putting a nosebag on Urbino, the starved old grey he used, as it dozed under an army blanket in the shafts of its cart. All round them bricklayers clad in scraps of uniform and hats made out of newspaper were rebuilding bombed houses from the old bricks of ruined ones, and the air resounded to the clatter of buckets and the clink of trowels, even here and there a snatch of song in a soaring Italian tenor where some man, uplifted by the ascent from disaster, felt obliged to give vent to his feelings.

Mori stared at the hearse, puzzled. 'But that,' he pointed out, 'is a hearse. Despite the whitewash, it is still a hearse. Whose?'

'Yours,' Pugh said. 'The man it belonged to doesn't want it. All you have to do is keep it stabled for the time being. Together with the box that's inside it.'

Mori was intrigued. 'There is something inside the box, of course?' he queried.

'Let's say, it's nothing that matters.'

'Secrets, perhaps?'

'Perhaps.'

'Perhaps even' – the old man smiled – 'tinned beef, tinned milk. Things of this nature.'

'Perhaps.'

Mori gestured. 'Have no fear, Signor Sergente. Your secret is safe with me.'

'Look after it, then the horse, the hearse and the box will eventually become yours. How would you like to become an undertaker?'

The old man seemed doubtful. 'I have no experience of funerals,' he said.

'I have,' Foscari pointed out.

'To be an undertaker, one must know the business.'

'I do.'

'How to build coffins? Where to obtain flowers? How to make wreaths and sprays? How to handle the business?'

'I know it all.' Foscari held up the bag containing the coffin handles from the police ambush and the stolen fitments from Ciasca's hearse that had been returned to them by Chief Renza. 'And I have here everything we need. I am an expert. It is my trade. Before the war I worked for my uncle in Caserta. All I wanted was to get back to it. But he is dead now and the business is sold. All I need is a place to cut wood.'

When Pugh left them, they were working out the terms of what looked like being a successful partnership.

Captain Jones wasn't in his office when Pugh appeared but he arrived soon afterwards. He looked more cheerful than normal.

'We've started winning the war,' he said. 'They've landed in Normandy. News came through this morning and it's just been confirmed.'

He wasn't as excited as he might have been over D-Day, because they'd been having D-Days in Italy ever since they'd landed in Sicily. They'd been calling themselves the D-Day Dodgers, in fact, to counteract the feeling that the campaign in Italy had been obscured by the assault on France with its greater propaganda value.

'Now that we've got Rome,' Jones said, 'they'll forget us. Did you get the paintings?'

'Seven of them,' Pugh said.

191

'Why not twelve?'

'We had a few brushes with people here and there. Germans, for a start. Then Corneliano and the partisans. Finally the police and a mad *goumier*. We lost five.'

He explained what had happened but Jones didn't seem over-worried. 'Not a bad batting average,' he said. 'Under the conditions. But I don't think Tasker's going to be pleased.'

'I don't want Tasker to know,' Pugh said. 'Not yet, anyway.'

'Why not?'

As Pugh outlined his suspicions, Jones listened with sympathy. He sat quietly at his desk, his fingers together to make a steeple, smoking his pipe and saying nothing. When Pugh had finished, he knocked out his pipe and looked up.

'I think we'd better get that signal off to London,' he said. 'In the meantime, I'll see the general and warn him what we're up to, so that if anything happens we can bring him in as a witness. No names, though, so no pack drills. I don't give a damn whom you suspect, but we're naming no one yet. I've grown to like Naples and I want to stay here a little longer.'

Leaving Jones, Pugh called in at a bar and had a beer. It was poor stuff but he needed it. Then he began to think of Tamara again and wondered if she was taking proper precautions. He had a feeling that the three paintings she possessed were going to be the most valuable of the whole Detto Banti collection, and he decided to see what she had done with them.

Her apartment was still chilly despite the end of the cold weather and she hadn't bothered to remove her coat. Looking at her in the old army blanket garment, Pugh thought how splendid she would look in a good one. She met him with a smile that showed she was pleased to see him. On the table she had arranged the few knicknacks belonging to Bocco Detto Banti which they had recovered from Enrichetta's bag.

'I was just admiring them,' she said. 'I think they might be of value. I have a little coffee. I think it came from the Americans. But, of course, I was not aware when I bought it.' She smiled to indicate that she knew perfectly well, and that she knew he knew, that it was black market coffee and that, like everyone else in Italy, she had had no qualms about buying it because she needed to stay alive. 'I have also a bottle of strega. Perhaps you'll have a drink with me?'

'I'll have a drink with you,' Pugh agreed.

They began to talk about the remaining paintings.

'Do you think what are left are safe?' she asked.

'As safe as I can make them.'

'Must you report them to your officer?'

'I have done. But there are a lot of people after them. The Ministero di Belli Arti e Monumenti for a start, British Arts and Monuments, the American Fine Arts and Archives. I don't trust any of them. There are also Da Sangalla, De Castro and one or two AMGOT officers I wouldn't trust. Tassinari says they're yours and that's good enough for me. It's up to you to do what you wish with them.'

'You will advise me, perhaps?'

'I'll advise you. In the meantime, we'll leave them where they are until I can find out just who's prepared to pay for them and how much.'

She handed him his glass of strega and, as she did so, she reached up and kissed his cheek. 'You have been kind to me, Piu.'

He grinned at her. 'After all, we've been sharing a bed for a long time.'

'What happens now?'

He gestured at the rolled and parcelled still life. 'I find a reputable expert – one I can trust – and get him to give me an opinion. Then we decide what to do with the other pictures, where to sell them – and to whom. Have you the three small ones safe?'

'They'll not be found.' Her eyes lifted to the top of the tall cupboard in the kitchen.

'On top of there?'

'No.'

Then he noticed the small trapdoor in the ceiling just above it.

'Up there?'

'Yes. It was hard work getting them up. It involved using the steps, then sitting on top and pushing open the trapdoor.'

'What's it like up there.'

'Dusty. There are probably also bats. I was terrified.'

'I meant temperature. Is it dry? Reasonably warm?'

'As warm as anywhere in Naples at the moment. I wrapped them up in an old coat. They're safe for a while. I hope it won't be longer than that.'

Outside the Casa Calafati, where Pugh's room was situated, a big car was waiting. A man was sitting in it, his coat collar up, his hat down, a handkerchief to his face. Pugh had a vague feeling that there was something odd about the car, but it wasn't strong enough for him to think about it for more than a second.

The Contessa appeared as he reached the stairs. Her eyes were circled with shadows and she held a cigarette between her fingers, coughing as if about to give up the ghost.

'You are back,' she said. 'You have been a long time. I nearly let your room. But you have a guest. He awaits.'

He produced a sausage for her that he had managed to buy in Sili and she went into noisy raptures of delight. Kissing her on the cheek, he left her almost swooning and headed up the stairs.

On the landing, he was surprised to find Marco waiting by his door. Pugh regarded him with suspicion.

'What are you after?'

'A talk.'

'What about?'

'The painting.' Marco gestured at the rolled package Pugh carried, and it was in Pugh's mind that he was wanting to make some deal that would deprive Tamara of it.

'I've already made arrangements for it,' he said.

'I suppose you have. But I'd still like to talk. And I wouldn't mind a drink, if you've got one. Even just a coffee.'

Pugh's flat was in darkness and, as he switched the light on, the usual small bulb high in the ceiling lit up. The Italians were always over-cautious with their light bulbs – as though they were afraid that anything bigger than two candlepower would explode and destroy them – and they normally used a forty-watt bulb to light places as big as ballrooms.

He unrolled the painting and, placing it on one of the chairs, stared at it for a while, then he turned to the gas ring to make a hot drink.

Marco studied the painting sombrely. 'That's a good picture,' he said slowly.

'The best of the lot,' Pugh agreed.

'That's what I came to see you about. I'd like it. If I'm to get any, that's the one I'd like.'

Pugh didn't answer, and had just finished boiling water when there was a knock on the door. He turned off the gas – it was so weak it could barely crawl out of the burner – and went to answer it. As he reached the door, the knock came again. As he opened it, he saw Da Sangalla outside.

'Sergeant Pugh,' he said.

'I'm busy,' Pugh said.

He was about to close the door when Da Sangalla pushed his foot forward to jam it and used his shoulder to force it wide. Immediately the flat seemed to be filled with soldiers. They were in Italian uniform and they all carried weapons. Da Sangalla followed them in. His uniform, as usual, was immaculate. Marco looked scared.

Pugh indicated the soldiers. There were six of them and a sergeant.

'Friends of yours?' he asked.

'I represent the Ministero di Monumenti e Belli Arti,' Da Sangalla said. 'And in my brief is a clause that if necessary I can call on the army for support.'

'We all have that,' Pugh said. 'Amazing how everybody thinks alike.'

'They are here to sort things out if there should be any resistance to my demands.'

'Which are?'

'You know what they are.'

'I can guess. I'm wondering why, that's all.'

Pugh glanced through the window. The car was still there, the man in it still holding his handkerchief to his face.

'Your friend has a cold?' he asked.

'He isn't well.'

'Is he there to give advice? It's De Castro, isn't it?'

Da Sangalla feigned surprise. 'Is it? I think he's merely out to take the air. My car is further down the road.' He smiled. 'You know why I'm here, of course.'

'Of course.'

'I have come for the Detto Bantis.'

'Tough tit. They've gone.'

De Sangalla gestured at the *Still Life with Chessmen*. 'That's one, Sergeant.'

Pugh stared at the picture. It was obviously pointless disputing the fact and it seemed more sensible to admit it and guard the remainder.

'That's the only one.'

'What happened to the rest?'

'I don't know. There were six. That's the last. The Germans helped themselves, so did the Resistance. They'll have sent the proceeds to the Communist Party in Rome, I expect. Perhaps even to Uncle Joe Stalin himself. Corneliano got one, and unfortunately, when he was shot, it disappeared, so if it comes on the market you'll know it's genuine. It's called *A Stolen Embrace*. Lascivious-looking chap with his paw on a girl's left tit.'

'There were others?'

'True. Two were destroyed. One was shot to pieces by the Germans and one was destroyed by a mad *goumier*. There was one other which was given away.'

'To whom?'

Pugh smiled. 'You could buy it if you wished. It's at the Orphanage of the Virgin of Manimora at Moccino.'

Da Sangalla smiled. 'I think they'll be willing to sell.'

Pugh smiled back at him. 'I think they might. But you'll have to pay what it's worth. They know its value because I told them, and they'll drive a hard bargain.'

Da Sangalla frowned. 'And the rest?'

Pugh indicated the *Still Life*. 'That's the rest. One painting. And it's going where it belongs.'

'I think not.' Da Sangalla said. 'One is a poor return for all the trouble I've taken, but it will be enough. I know where I can sell it. And it won't be to Colonel Tasker or Colonel Baracca. That would be silly. They would never pay its full value.'

'Neither, I suspect, will you.'

'Then you might just as well let me have it. You have no option, Sergeant, anyway.'

Glancing through the window, Pugh saw that the man in the car had climbed out. He was crossing the road now, the handkerchief still to his face. He smiled.

'I think your friend wants you,' he said. Da Sangalla glanced through the window, nodded to the Italian sergeant, and slipped out to the landing. Pugh could hear them talking. As they waited, he suddenly heard Marco whispering.

'Let him have it,' he was saying. 'It's not a Detto Banti.' Pugh turned and stared at Marco. 'It isn't,' Marco insisted softly. 'I know it isn't.'

For a moment Pugh wondered if he were in league somehow with Da Sangalla and that was the reason why he had turned up for a chat. But Marco shook his head again. 'It isn't,' he repeated. 'I swear it on the head of my dead brother.'

Da Sangalla reappeared in the doorway and they heard slow footsteps on the stairs outside. After a while, as Da Sangalla stared at the painting, Pugh saw the man with the handkerchief return to the car, climb in and be driven off.

Pugh smiled. 'Going to make an offer?'

Da Sangalla smiled. 'No, Sergeant. We have no guarantee that the picture is genuine.'

'You're playing with fire, Da Sangalla,' Pugh said. 'You'll never get away with it. Tasker and Baracca will be after you at once.'

'They'll be too late. I shall have disappeared by the time they learn what's happened.'

'You'll be finished as an art dealer.'

'I'm not worried. I don't have to be, with a million lire in my pocket.'

'Half that,' Pugh smiled. 'De Castro will want a cut.'

Da Sangalla frowned and Pugh guessed that he had already worked out some scheme whereby he could disappear and leave De Castro in the cold. Da Sangalla produced a large-denomination note and laid it on the table. 'Take this, Sergeant, for your trouble.'

'It's not worth much in my country.'

Da Sangalla smiled and picked up the still life. 'Doubtless you'll manage.'

'What makes you think I shan't report what's happened to Tasker and Baracca?'

'I'm not worried about Tasker and Baracca.'

The words set Pugh thinking. Had Da Sangalla access to some secret shady business Tasker and Baracca were involved in, so that he could threaten them if they tried to move against him? He watched Da Sangalla study the picture and roll it up.

'At first glance,' he said, 'a very good Detto Banti. Not typical but good nevertheless.'

He gestured to the sergeant and the soldiers, who

filed out. Da Sangalla waited in the entrance. 'The sergeant will be waiting outside for ten minutes,' he said. 'I prefer you not to follow me.'

Pugh watched the door close, then he turned to Marco. 'How do you know it isn't a Detto Banti?' he said at once.

Marco grinned. 'Because I painted a lot of it myself.'

There was a long silence, then Pugh lit a cigarette and handed the packet to Marco.

'When?' he said.

'Just before his last illness. He was still trying. He needed the money, and a painting was the only way to raise some. But he couldn't finish it. So I took over. I told you, I'd often painted bits of other pictures. I knew his style. Hardly any of it's Bocco's work.' Marco smiled. 'Funny, isn't it? You decided to sell Bocco's paintings on the strength of one that he didn't paint. He spent all his life sneering at my little efforts, but in the end it was to be my work that was to establish the genuineness of *his* work.'

'One of life's little ironies,' Pugh said.

'What'll you do? About Da Sangalla, I mean.'

'He'll never get away with it. Tasker and Baracca will have every military policeman and field security organisation in the American and British armies looking for him. De Castro too.'

'Will they take it off him?'

'Without doubt.' Pugh was thoughtful. 'And, since you painted most of it, you might well end up as the owner. Pity it's not a genuine Detto Banti. It might have fetched more money.'

5

Jones's request to the general for confirmation that the government in London were interested in the Detto Banti canvasses brought a quick reply. But it came from an unexpected source – a department of the War Office dealing with the high incidence of looting in occupied countries – and it requested to know more about the Detto Bantis.

Jones beamed at Pugh and agreed to accompany him to see Colonel Tasker.

'We'd better go into this together,' he said. 'He'll probably court-martial me and shoot you, but I'll enjoy seeing his reaction. Got your story ready?'

He made an appointment, giving an indication of what it was about, and the following day they drove to Tasker's office in Jones's Jeep. For once there was no need to send a message to the O Sole Mio bar. There was no sign of Tasker's car outside as they drove up, though Pugh noticed that Cirri's hearse was in the yard as usual and his horse tied to the lamp post, with a nosebag attached to its head.

Colonel Baracca was with Tasker, and they were both looking smart, with the smartness of men who worked an eight-hour day in an office with long lunch breaks and no overtime.

Tasker smiled as they entered. 'Sergeant,' he said. 'Have you got the Detto Bantis?'

Pugh glanced at Jones.

'He found himself in some danger,' Jones said at once. 'And I have to register a protest that he was sent there.'

'Bit late for that now, Captain,' Tasker said cheerfully. 'What about the Detto Bantis?'

'He didn't get them.'

Tasker's rosy glow fell away like the curtains at the end of a performance. 'Why not?'

'You'd better hear it from Sergeant Pugh.'

Tasker stared at Pugh with eyes that were like the barrels of twin machine guns. Pugh was aware of Baracca, sitting alongside Tasker's desk, also staring hard at him. He hadn't moved – Baracca never seemed to move much – but his amber eyes were suddenly hard.

'Well, go on,' Tasker snapped.

'I understood,' Pugh said, 'that there were twelve pictures.'

'There were.'

'No, there weren't. There were six. The brother who laid the information was lying in the hope of a big reward.'

Tasker was silent for a while, his face red, his eyes angry. 'Where is this brother now?' he snapped eventually.

'He headed for Brindisi. He has relatives there.'

'Name?'

'Bonti. Via Conoso, 105.' The lie came easily. 'That's the address he gave me.'

Tasker wrote the address on a pad. 'We'll check on him. He probably kept the others himself. What about the remaining six? Where are they?'

'Nowhere. There aren't any.'

'What?' Even Baracca was on his feet this time, and Pugh continued, enjoying every minute.

'We were cut off in Vicinamontane,' he said. 'But we got the pictures away – all that we could find – in a hearse.'

'In a hearse?'

'How would you have done it, sir?' Pugh asked innocently. 'In a pantechnicon marked "Art Treasures"?'

'Don't be bloody insolent, Sergeant! Get on with it.'

'We were stopped by Germans returning from Croci-fisso. They were removing the Tintoretto *Adoration*.

201

They'd already removed the altarpiece from Avizano. However, I happened to learn where they're being taken to.'

Baracca's eyes gleamed. 'Where?'

'Austria. Captain Jones has the exact address. He's passed it on to the general.'

Tasker's face went red. 'And the pictures?'

'Four were lost when the Germans were attacked by partisans. One was stolen by Corneliano, the bandit.'

'They shot him.'

'But they didn't recover the picture.'

'I'll bet the bloody police collared it,' Tasker snarled.

'That was a thought that crossed my mind.'

'And the other? There's still one. What happened to that?'

'Colonel da Sangalla, of the Ministero di Monumenti e Belli Arti, removed that one from my room. At gunpoint.'

Tasker glared. He looked like a lion at feeding time thwarted of its dinner. 'It doesn't belong to the bloody Italian Government!' he snapped. 'It belongs to us.'

'That's what I told him,' Pugh smiled. 'He insisted, though, and I don't argue with a gun. Not when all I'm armed with is a revolver with which I couldn't hit a pig in a passage.'

Tasker was already reaching for the telephone. 'Where's Da Sangalla now?'

'Doubtless in hiding. But you could possibly find out from Sergio de Castro.'

'The dealer?'

'The very same.'

'We'll let them pick up Da Sangalla,' Jones said cheerfully as they left. 'Then we'll let them know his painting isn't a Detto Banti at all. That should please everybody all round. Is this brother really in Brindisi?'

'He's here in Naples. In hiding.'

Jones smiled and suggested they have a drink. They

found a bar and, parking the Jeep within two feet of the table where they were sitting so no one could steal it or any part of it, they sat back with a vermouth each.

'Give them a little longer,' Pugh suggested. 'Let Da Sangalla buy the one we left at the Orphanage of the Virgin of Manimora. I dare bet he expects to sell it to an American for twice what he'll have to pay for it.'

'Personally,' Jones said, 'I'll be glad when these bloody Detto Bantis are out of the way. I need you.'

'Too many girls wanting to marry British soldiers?'

'I wish that were all. It's your penicillin, old lad. And not just penicillin. Drugs in general. They keep disappearing. Whole consignments from the docks. Half the dock police are receiving hand-outs to look the other way, and now that Rome's fallen it gives the bastards a wider market. They can even send the stuff up by sea to Civitavecchia. The military police are checking, but so far we've found nothing. Just a few small packets, hidden in the cistern of the captain's cabin of a coaster. They'd go in your pocket, and we know there's more than that.'

Jones frowned. 'There's plenty else, too,' he went on. 'God knows how many political parties for a start, all clamouring to be allowed to hold meetings and all expecting to be in power when the elections are held. Only the Christian Democrats, the Socialists and the Communists really count, of course, and even the Communists don't count for much. They're like a tadpole – all head and no tail. Mind you, they aren't really expecting much. They think the Christian Democrats will win and be so corrupt they'll be chucked out, so the Communists will have the opportunity to get in, in their place. They've a hope! The Yanks would never allow it.' Jones fiddled with his glass for a moment. 'In addition,' he continued, 'it's still thought there are Teds hiding in the catacombs at San Placido. Noises are still heard and there's a panic that they're being fed by Fascist sympathisers and will sally out, now

203

that Rome's fallen, to cut our supply lines. I don't believe a word of it myself. The noises are probably just made by shifting earth. With Vesuvius close by, I reckon this whole bloody city's due to drop into a damn great hole at any moment.'

He finished his drink. 'In the meantime, I have to go down to Reggio di Calabria. We think drugs are being brought across from North Africa to Sicily in troopships – probably by stewards – and then across to the mainland from Messina. I shall be back on Saturday. I'm taking the train. As senior sergeant—'

'I'm not senior sergeant. Waddilove is.'

'Waddilove's in hospital.'

'Since when?'

'Since last night. He put his foot in a hole in the road – you know how the bastards pinch the manhole covers – and he's broken his leg. Just as well, as a matter of fact, because he's been sticking his finger into a little fiddle over tinned meat and he'll be going home. So you're running the place until I get back. I shall arrive on the midday train and I'll need meeting with the Jeep.'

The next few days were busy. There was a visit to be made to the Ufficio Matricola, where prisoners at the prison at Poggio Reale were admitted or discharged, and a trip to Ischia to interview a small-time crook with a grudge who said he was prepared to give evidence against a big-timer they had been chasing for months. It happened to be a public holiday and the ferry was crammed with people armed with guitars and trumpets and old shoe-boxes containing picnic lunches. They swarmed all over the ship, some of the young men, show-offs like so many Italians, even climbing the rails and clinging to the outside.

When they reached Ischia Porto, an old man who looked like Tassinari promptly offered to take them to their witness. Within seconds, however, it was clear he had battened on to them in the hope of getting something to eat. Pugh bought him a coffee and a roll, and he was so tearfully grateful he allowed them to continue alone to their witness, who, it appeared, had suddenly got the wind up and, afraid of retaliation from the big-timer's friends, had decided against giving evidence, after all. The old man was on the ferry going back and, for another cup of coffee, gave Pugh the whole history of the Campi Flegri and its associated legends.

There was also an epidemic of telephone-wire cutting, for which the excuse was that the Allies had told the Italians to do that very thing to harass the Germans and they'd never been told to stop. There were instructions that precautions against typhoid were to be intensified and that sanitary teams would be on the streets, using an anti-typhus spray on any likely subject. There was also to be a campaign against flies and yet another against promiscuity – what the troops called the Lechery Law. Bullied and wheedled, the Italians could only hit back by demanding that their women should be left alone, and once again the British were trying to follow the example of the Americans, who were already conducting – not very successfully, it had to be admitted – a campaign to improve morals. Imagining that this new campaign would go the same way as all the others, Pugh tossed the instructions into Jones's 'in' tray for him to study when he came back. He fully expected Jones would do nothing about it because he never had before.

There was also a 'contessa' who had put on a show of wealth to persuade a British officer to marry her, and had then been found to have a husband already, elderly and infirm and safely tucked away in the north behind the German lines; and a prince who indignantly claimed his sister was using his palazzo to run a high-class brothel for officers. There were other things, too – the line-crossers who were paid to take letters to relatives in the north but in fact dumped them at the first opportunity; a dockworker caught stealing tins of meat – for his family, he said, which was probably true; and a little gang who were gaining entry to houses by posing as American welfare workers seeking suitable premises for soldiers' clubs – as one half of the group was being shown round, the other half robbed the place of everything they could lay their hands on. All this was in addition to the quacks who claimed to be able to provide women anxious to marry British soldiers with toned-up sexual organs, crooks working on the superstitions of the poor to offer fake medicines and holy relics, witnesses who were known to have seen a man blown up by a bomb in front of them but, because they were afraid of retribution from the gangs, claimed to have observed nothing of it.

Pugh found he was too busy coordinating the enquiries of the other sergeants to have much time for his own enquiries. With Waddilove gone, there was extra work and, just to help matters, the day before Jones was due to return, an officer from the Commission for the Protection of Arts and Monuments arrived, wanting to know where the Detto Bantis were. Pugh and O'Mara were dealing with the case of a soldier who had stolen a consignment of Scotch whisky. This had involved O'Mara in getting a little drunk, so that he was singing softly when the door opened.

'Hitler has only got one ball,
Goering has two, but very small,
Himmler is very sim'lar,
And Goe-balls has no balls at all—'

'Come in, you darlin' man, sor,' he said as the officer stuck his head round the door.

He was a young man called Grafton-Smith who looked as if he'd just left a seminary, but he was a captain nevertheless, and, disgusted to learn that the Detto Bantis were not in their possession, he let them know his views in no uncertain terms.

206

'Do you mean to say,' he demanded, 'that you let the bloody things slip through your fingers? Art and museum experts in uniform are following the Allied armies with the sole purpose of tracking down looted art treasures like these. We follow clues that are often no more than rumours.'

'What do you think *I've* been doing?' Pugh snapped.

'We've come to Europe as liberators, not conquerors,' Grafton-Smith went on. 'So we have to preserve the goodwill and cooperation of the occupied peoples. They need their pride to be restored, and this means their treasures have to be located and returned. The bloody Nazis picked Poland clean in six months. They aren't the supermen everybody imagined; they're just predatory hooligans.'

Neither Pugh nor O'Mara cared for the smooth-faced young officers like Grafton-Smith who were beginning to arrive in numbers in Italy – and doubtless other places, too, now that the front in France had been opened. They were all full of bright ideas about how the world should be run and, following hard on the heels of the fighting troops, succeeded only in making a nuisance of themselves.

'We should slap an order on the pictures,' Grafton-Smith insisted. 'The work's going to be given high priority by us.'

'It's *always* had priority with us.'

'Hitler—'

'Who's he?' O'Mara asked.

Pugh grinned. 'He's nobody from here.'

Grafton-Smith glared. 'Are all FS sergeants as rude as you two?'

'Most of 'em,' O'Mara said. 'Though *we're* very good at it.'

'You should remember what you're dealing with. Hitler would steal anything. When he went into Prague in 1939, he left the Hradčány Castle with a couple of tapestries rolled up and stuffed into his car like a hotel guest pinching a towel.'

The indignant Grafton-Smith had no sooner left than an American lieutenant in rimless glasses appeared on the same quest.

'Leroy Hatton,' he introduced himself. 'Art Looting Investigation Unit of the US Office of Strategic Services. Recruited, commissioned and trained in America. We're super-detectives,' he added modestly, 'Carrying out a unique task in history.'

He, too, had no direct orders but he'd also heard of the Detto Bantis and was anxious to get hold of them.

'You wouldn't believe what's been stolen,' he said. 'We've picked up photograph albums with the words *Gemälderei Linz* – Linz Collection – marked on 'em in gold. They show pictures earmarked for this goddam treasurehouse Hitler wants to build up in his birthplace. They say it's because he was spurned as an artist in Vienna as a young man.' Hatton slapped his thigh. 'Hell, that guy couldn't paint a front door! They list old masters, Dutch, Flemish, Italian, German – not many English, he didn't like Limey painters – tapestries, artifacts, marbles, statuary, armour, coins, rare books. They got the Rothschild and Schwartzenberg collections. They've got the Czernin Vermeer, Holbeins, Rembrandts, Tintorettos, the Hohenfürth altarpiece from the Sudetenland, Rubenses, Goyas, Watteaus, Fragonards, the goddam lot! There are photographs of them all, and we know now that they're being taken to Austria. All we have to do is find them.'

'They wouldn't want Detto Bantis,' Pugh said.

'Oh, yeah? That's what you think. What are they worth?'

Pugh was suspicious of both officers. They seemed to care far more about value than about art, and he wondered how much they were hoping to acquire on the side for themselves.

In the morning, he went to see a Professor Arco of the Fine Art Department at the university, whom Tassinari had recommended to give an honest opinion on the Detto Bantis. He was a thin little man with a shock of white hair and a white goatee beard and moustache. He had no interest in the Detto Bantis himself because he had never liked the painter.

'He was after Fascist patronage,' he said sharply. 'And that isn't art, not even if the Fascists had known anything about art, which they didn't. I would not recommend buying him. He had too many periods, most of them bad, interspersed – very occasionally – with a good one when he painted something worthwhile. His best period was in England. When he returned to Italy, he was already past his best. He painted nothing of note here.'

'Would you buy one as a normal collector?'

'I wouldn't. But there are many who would.'

'At what price?'

'I have no idea. I would place them around a million to two million lire.'

A dealer Pugh saw had different ideas. 'Four million,' he said at once. 'If they're good, five million. Perhaps even six. It depends on the quality.'

'Would there be any difficulty selling one?'

Bright black eyes gleamed. 'Have you got one?'

Well, Pugh thought, that was all right. Tamara was not going to come out of things too badly in the end. And he was suddenly concerned that she shouldn't. She had been remarkably brave about the losses they had sustained, her only unhappiness that part of her heritage had gone.

'Would you be prepared to look at the pictures?' he asked.

'If necessary.'

'What do you need?'

The dealer smiled. 'Just my eyes,' he said. 'It would be different if Detto Banti had painted 200 years ago because hand-ground colours are coarse by comparison with modern ones and artificial craquelure can't stand examination. Even the dirt isn't the same as centuries of dust. The old master racket's finished.' The bright black eyes suddenly looked anxious. 'I trust you have your paintings safe, Sergeant. There are a lot of people in Naples who are aware that paintings are valuable. Prices are going up and they're going up more all the time. I hope they're nowhere anyone can steal them.'

Early the following day there was a tremendous explosion in the Via Bontinani. It brought down a house in a torrent of bricks and blew in windows for a hundred yards around. Pugh felt the shock in his room in the Casa Calafati and immediately set off to see what he could do to help. The street was full of rubble, with fragments of stone and marble scattered everywhere. There wasn't a window with any glass in it, not a shutter left on any wall in the street. The explosion had occurred near a queue of shoppers, and thinking he could see a body, he moved towards it only to find it was one of the statues from a public garden nearby. British, American, Canadian, French and Polish soldiers were struggling with the Italian police to pull wounded people from under the rubble. The air was filled with wailings, and they were laying a row of dead children in the roadway like dusty broken dolls. A woman, beheaded by the blast, lay in the gutter. The body of another had been thrown on to the sagging telegraph wires.

It was thought it was a German device, because during the liberation of the city, when the Germans had wrecked harbour installations, sewers, water conduits, gas, light and water works, delayed-action mines had been left behind to go off at intervals. One had gone off in the post office, killing a hundred civilians, and another had been found in the only undamaged hotel in the city, which the United States general commanding the 5th Army had inevitably selected for his head-quarters.

Men, women and children, their clothes half-stripped

from them by the blast, their faces covered with blood and white plaster dust, were picking their way dazedly through the ruins. There was a lot of panic talk that more mines would go off in the evening after dark, when the peak period for the electricity works was reached. Although in the end it was discovered that the disaster had been caused not by a mine but by an unexploded bomb disturbed by workmen digging their way to a damaged water main, an exodus from the city was already taking place. By the time the panic had died down and loud hailers were being used to damp down the excitement, Pugh was as filthy as everybody else, his uniform covered with blood and torn where he had caught it on splintered wood or twisted steel.

He returned to his room, bathed in tepid water, changed and handed his dirty uniform to the Contessa to be washed. When he reached his office, a letter was waiting for him from the Mother Superior of the Orphanage of the Virgin of Manimora. Her delight seemed to sparkle out of the page.

'We have sold the picture,' she announced. 'A man came who called himself Signor Sangalla and brought with him an expert whom I noticed he addressed as De Castro. They asked to see the picture. The man De Castro examined the paint – he seemed very concerned with the green of the clothing – and finally pronounced that it was Detto Banti green and that the painting was genuine. They offered a derisory sum of money, which, as you advised, I refused. There was a lot of argument but I produced the documents you had provided and put my trust in honesty and righteousness and refused to budge. Then – may the Holy Father forgive me! – I told them there was an American who wanted the picture and was prepared to pay the sum we were asking. There was a lot more talk and eventually they offered us 100,000 lire less than we asked, and this was so little a difference I accepted. I called in a priest and a notary and had everything signed and witnessed. They weren't pleased, but I insisted. Now that the picture is no longer my responsibility I am a great deal happier.'

Pugh almost crowed with pleasure and, dragging out a sheet of paper he wrote back, sending his congratulations both on the sale and on the wisdom of getting rid of the canvas.

'Take care to keep all documents locked up,' he warned. 'There are some strange people about.'

That evening, he heard that De Castro had been arrested by the military police and that an order had gone out for the arrest of Da Sangalla. He was satisfied. Things seemed to be working out well, and he pulled the motor bicycle off its stand and rode out to see Mori and Foscari.

Outside the stable now was an elaborate sign: 'Funeral Arrangements. Decorous. Dignified. Modest Prices.' Beneath it was a little workshop where Foscari was building coffins, and arranging wreaths from flowers which Pugh knew he bought cheaply from florists who couldn't sell them to anyone else. Mori was preparing for a funeral and was dressed in a greasy gold-braided coat and cap ready to drive his hearse about his business. They greeted Pugh with wide smiles.

'We still have your goods, Signor Sergente,' Mori said. 'They are safe. When do you come to collect them?'

'I don't. Not yet. I came to make sure they're safe.'

Foscari was delighted to be home and Mori, who was a widower, had welcomed him into his business with open arms. They had already conducted two funerals – cheap ones, because they worked from a cheap part of the city – and they felt they were established.

'We are prospering already,' Mori said. 'Fiorello is a good stable companion to Urbino, and people have been to look at the hearse to be sure it's fit to carry their dead.'

They accepted the bomb explosion with the usual Italian sadness but with barely concealed pleasure that it had brought them work.

212

'It's a time for dying in Naples,' Foscari said. 'There were three people killed from this area alone, and everyone with a hearse is busy just now. One of the dead was an old man aged seventy-six from the Via Coppi. He served through the last war on the Austrian front. On Wednesday there's a child. How they die these days! Half the funerals are children.'

Pugh knew it only too well. Every day, funerals trailed through the shabby streets, white coffins on hand-carts or carried by two men and followed by wailing women tearing with their nails at their cheeks and stumbling in front of a huge wreath which would have set the family heavily in debt. The long strings of mourners, relatives, neighbours and friends, determined not to miss the show of grief, always totally ignored the traffic as they wound in and out of the trams and trolley buses and the army lorries nudging impatiently past to get on with the war.

'Tomorrow,' Mori went on, 'we have a big order. We are to do a job for Armando Cirri. He has three funerals and has asked us to do one. He will pay well and it may be the beginning of a long association.'

Pugh remembered Cirri, who tied his horse to the lamp post outside the O Sole Mio. 'Who's dead?' he asked.

'Old man. Name of Gustavo Grei. Not a complete job with flowers. Just to the station. The coffin goes to Rome, where it will be met by the family and the body interred in a family plot there. It's fortunate that Rome is in our hands again, otherwise he would have had to be buried here.'

On Thursday evening, Pugh arranged to take Tamara out to a meal by the harbour. She appeared wearing a blue velvet dress, her face radiant.

'The curtains!'

She nodded, delighted that he had recognised them. 'I have had them cleaned. They are a little heavy in this weather but they will keep me warm in winter.'

213

Pugh grinned. 'I think having a lot of money will suit you,' he said.

The following midday, he was at the station with the Jeep to pick up Jones. He took a driver with him so that nobody would steal the wheels while he went to the platform to meet Jones. Anything was possible in Naples. One officer who had left his vehicle in a back street had returned to find the tyres stolen by children and, while searching for new tyres, had lost the wheels. By the time he had managed to place a guard on the vehicle, the engine had been removed.

As he moved towards the platform, past the pink-painted station buildings, to ask information of the train from the south, a crowd was gathering on the Rome platform and the railway officials were looking worried.

'It'll be a riot,' one of them said. 'Now that Rome's been liberated, everybody wants to go. It's amazing how many people have discovered they have business or relatives there.' He gestured at a group of policemen standing near the waiting room, their faces expression-less, their caps over their eyes in the way all Italian police seemed to wear their caps. 'Everybody in Rome wants to come to Naples and everybody in Naples wants to go to Rome. And as we're still only running a shuttle service, it'll be the same train, so there'll be a million people trying to get on a train that will have a million people trying to get off.'

Even as Pugh turned away, the train arrived with a howl like a banshee and the uproar started at once. Packed with people wanting to go north to the capital, the platform became a madhouse of screaming, push-ing, fighting figures, and Pugh was swept aside at once. Remembering to keep one hand on his wallet and one on his revolver, he was spun round, barged from side to side, and finally ejected like a pip from an orange to the rear of the platform alongside the policemen. As the train slowed, people on the platform determined to find a seat began to scramble aboard even before the train

214

had stopped, and the corridors became jammed with shrieking passengers trying to get into compartments which were still crowded with passengers trying to get out. Suitcases were pushed, even thrown, through windows, and a fight between two men in a third-class corridor turned into a screeching bedlam that emptied compartments all round and sent a couple of policemen running down the platform.

Outside a first-class compartment, there was a shoving match between two stout men and around them another riot was building up. Someone pushed someone else and a fist flew, and in no time two men were on the floor and a woman was trying to beat a youth's head down between his shoulders with an umbrella. People were pushing wives through windows, shrieking at them to find a place before they were all taken, and screaming children clutching parcels were in danger of being trampled on.

Then suddenly the yelling inside the train stopped. The silence spread and the crowd parted. A man held the door open and another moved officiously between the crowd, pushing them back. More men stood with their arms out to hold the crowd so that there was a clear pathway between them, and there was a reverent quiet as a young woman clutching a baby in her arms stepped from the train. Hats came off and everyone became silent. Bad temper vanished and there were smiles all round. Even the baby seemed to be smiling but, then, you never heard babies crying in Italy, because when an Italian baby showed signs of bursting into tears, there was always the mother, a big sister, an aunt, a cousin, a grandmother, to pick it up and comfort it.

Gradually the uproar died, leaving only a few dazed people and a scattering of belongings. A man, jammed into a compartment he daren't leave for fear of losing his place, stuck his head through the window to appeal for someone to pass him his hat, which lay, battered and trodden on, on the platform, where there were parcels, items of clothing, even one or two shoes. Heading for the exit, Pugh handed the hat to the frantic owner. It was received with effusive thanks, and Pugh had just reached the exit when he saw a procession crossing the pavement to the station entrance.

It consisted of a coffin carried by Foscari, old Mori and four attendants, all dressed in threadbare black coats and ties, and frayed white shirts. The coffin was of good wood and decorated with chrome fittings and, even with six people to carry it, seemed heavy enough to make them struggle.

Behind the hearse a large black car had drawn up and from it three men were climbing. Pugh, standing among a group of carabinieri, drew back into a doorway as the men strode forward, their faces blank and expressionless. They were all dressed in well-pressed suits with broad black bands on their arms. They carried their hats against their chests and their leader had a medal ribbon on his lapel which Pugh immediately recognised as the first essential of the uncle from Rome. The number plate of the car was a Roman one but, with the difficulties of obtaining petrol and the fact that Rome had only recently been liberated, he guessed it was a false one on a local vehicle.

The platform had not yet emptied of people and, as the coffin passed, people engaged in gathering their families or their belongings straightened up. Hats tumbled and women crossed themselves. There was a general drawing back, partly out of respect, partly from superstition.

Reaching the guard's van, Mori and his helpers backed away as the coffin disappeared inside, then, standing by the open door, Foscari began to gesture with his arms as if he were a semaphore signaller, sending the four helpers off for the flowers. The guard and a whole army of porters were standing alongside a nearby first-class compartment, determined to keep it empty. The well-dressed men with the armbands

216

moved forward and one of them handed over a large-denomination note to the guard, who received it with a smile and a bow as they entered the compartment and pulled down the blinds.

Foscari saw Pugh as he turned away. 'Gustavo Grei,' he said. 'Going back to his family in Rome. A splendid coffin, *non è vero?* Just look at those fittings. Real chrome.'

'Did you put them on, Enzio?'

Foscari spread his hands. 'Not us. We haven't a stock of these things yet and they're hard to get. Soon, though. Cirri made the coffin. All we did was pick it up and bring it here.'

'He insisted on the greatest care,' Mori put in enthusiastically. 'And much reverence.' He indicated the four attendants still moving backwards and forwards with wreaths and large bunches of flowers, which they piled on top of the coffin. 'A fine funeral, Sergente. A fine funeral. But a heavy man. A very heavy man. Almost *too* heavy.' He gave a proud smile. 'But very profitable for us. A wealthy family, I understand. You will have noticed the uncle from Rome.' He grinned. 'This time, in fact, there was not only the uncle, there were two cousins as well.'

Pugh stood on the platform as they disappeared and was still there as the train pulled out. As the last coach vanished, he turned and hurried from the platform to meet the arrival from the south. His mind was racing, because the uncle from Rome who was gracing Gustavo Grei's funeral was the same rat-trap-mouthed man he had passed as he left the cell of the penicillin racketeer, Tirandolo, in the prison at Poggio Reale. He was wondering where the connection lay, because he was also the *sindaco* from Vicinamontane, Vicenzo Sansovino, who had uttered veiled threats over the Detto Banti canvasses.

6

Captain Jones was thirsty. The train from the south was crowded and hot, and the boy who carried the bottles of beer along the corridor had been left behind at Cosenza while trying to replenish his stock.

However, that was just one of those things that happened in wartime and Jones was chattering enthusiastically as they reached the station entrance. There was a small bar there, from which Foscari, Mori and two of their helpers were just appearing, wiping beer froth off their moustaches. The hearse stood waiting nearby, another attendant at its head, another at the rear to make sure no one stole anything. Old Fiorello seemed to recognise Pugh and gave a whinny of pleasure.

After dropping Jones, Pugh sought out Mori and Foscari again. Foscari was in the workshop giving *Tosca* a quick work-over, but he stopped, his face full of smiles, and, joined by old Mori, dug out the address from which they had picked up the corpse of Gustavo Grei.

'Via Maddalena 7,' Foscari said. 'Apartment 9.'

Number 7, Via Maddalena was a flat-fronted block of apartments near the university. It was neither wealthy nor poor, and the concierge told Pugh that Apartment 9 was still empty.

'He died,' he said. 'He was a strong old man, but I think the war put paid to him.'

'Was he wealthy?' Pugh asked.

'I wouldn't think so.'

'So who has the flat now?'

'No one, Signore. I have to sell the furniture and let it.'

'What about the relatives? Don't they want the furniture? Or the flat? Flats and furniture are hard to come by in Naples.'

'I have had no intimation to that effect, Signore.'

'What about children?'

'He was unmarried.'

'So who organised the funeral?'

'I don't know, Signore. I informed the police because I found him dead in bed. For the last year or so I always took him coffee and rolls upstairs. Then three days ago, I found him lying there. Later someone came and said the body would be removed by the undertaker. He came soon afterwards.'

'Who told you this? A relation?'

'*Si*, Signore. I assumed so. He lived here all his life.'

'Who are these relations? Do you have a name?'

'No, Signore.'

'Where can I get in touch with them?'

'I don't know that either, Signore. I heard them say they were leaving Naples after the funeral.'

'Did they go to Rome?'

'I assume so. They drove off. They got into a large car and disappeared without leaving an address.'

'Did they say when they were coming back?'

'No, Signore.'

'And the car? Whose was it?'

'Relatives? Friends? Perhaps the family has wealthy friends. They seem to have wealthy relatives. An uncle from Rome followed the coffin to the station with the relatives.'

'There were no relatives at the station,' Pugh said. 'No one but the uncle from Rome and two cousins. Have you the key to their flat?' He flashed his documents and the janitor's protest died away in a shrug.

'This way.'

The apartment looked very normal. It lay on the third floor of the block, up a grey staircase alongside a grey wall on which graffiti of various sorts had been

219

scrawled. It lay behind a heavy oak door, which was studded with bolts and looked strong enough to resist an attack by a tank and was obviously designed to withstand the depredations of the Neapolitan under-world.

Inside, it was just a normal flat – small, shabby, with battered furniture. Pugh moved around it, checking the drawers and cupboards, but there seemed to be nothing but the squirrel-like collecting of an old man. There were photographs of him in a uniform of the war of 1914–18 with a background of mountains; a few photographs of what Pugh assumed were nephews and nieces, all of them with no indication of who they were or where they lived; a few old newspapers; a few books, one or two of them pornographic; but nothing which gave a clue to why the far-from-rich dead man should have been given such a splendid funeral and accompanied to Rome by three well-dressed men, including one of Vito Genovese's appointed *sindacos*.

Was the dead man a friend of the gangsters who were running Naples? Was he a relation? Neapolitan sense of family was strong, and a poor relation, even a relation in no way involved with their activities, would be given a good send-off. But why send the body to Rome when Grei was unmarried and had lived in Naples all his life? It didn't make sense.

Pugh looked again at the photographs of the man in uniform with the mountains as his background.

'Grei,' he said. 'Was he a big man?'

The concierge shrugged. 'My size, Signore.'

The concierge had a typical Neapolitan figure – short, square and sturdy, but certainly not big or heavy.

'It was a big coffin,' Pugh said. 'And it looked heavy. When did it arrive?'

'The night before the funeral, Signore. It was delivered by the undertaker – Armando Cirri. A good undertaker, very careful of the correct things to do.'

'I'd have thought an experienced undertaker wouldn't

put a small man in a large coffin.'

'He didn't put the body in the coffin, Signore. The relatives did.'

Pugh's head turned. 'Oh? Why? Did they want him to lie in state? Did they want prayers? Did a priest come?'

'I saw no priest.'

'So why did he lie in state? Did anybody else come?'

'I saw no one. The coffin came. The undertaker left. Then the relatives left. The next morning a different undertaker came with a hearse, and the coffin was carried downstairs and the relations from Rome climbed into the car and off they went to the station.'

Climbing on the motor bike, Pugh sought out Cirri. He had just led his horse home from its parking place by the O Sole Mio bar. Outside his premises was an elaborate sign, *Pompe Funebri. Interramenti con dignità e decoro. Prezzi sotto costo.'

He was a small, fat man with a wide smile, still in the braided frock coat and top hat that he used for conducting funerals. As they talked, he removed the coat and hat, put on a pair of overalls and headed for a small workshop where an old man worked with a saw and sandpaper, his feet shuffling around in wood shavings. A small boy in cut-down clothes was collecting odds and ends of timber.

'For the fire,' Cirri said. 'Nothing must be wasted. Thank God we get our wood on good terms from the Busetti woodyard. They know I always pay and they make sure there's always some available for me.' He was talking quickly, almost as if he were nervous. 'A very busy time just now. Many people are dying. During the winter it was the cold and the hunger. Now, with the growing heat, it's the stomach.'

'Grei,' Pugh said, cutting into the torrent of words.

Cirri's eyes flickered nervously. The undertaker's shop was small, allowing room only for the display of one magnificently carved coffin partly draped in a black, skull-bedecked velvet pall like a Jolly Roger, and a large crucifix. It looked expensive, but even the poorest Neapolitan family would willingly reduce themselves to bitter want in order to bury one of their members with the best macabre trappings and necrophilistic embellishments their money could buy. Cirri seemed to find the place cramping, so he led the way to a small office, where he sat at a small table draped with another black-and-silver embroidered funeral pall. At his elbow was a vase of white flowers, rusting at the edges with age, and behind him was a background of palm leaves and fading wreaths.

'Grei,' Pugh said again.

Cirri smiled. 'A fine man,' he said. 'It was very sudden. They gave him a magnificent funeral.'

'Who did?'

'His relations?'

'And who were they?'

Cirri looked startled. 'I don't know. They said their name was Grei also.'

'Where did they come from?'

Cirri shrugged. 'How do I know, Signore?'

'Didn't you get an address?'

'They paid in cash. Its often done these days. The lira changes so often and some of the money – well!' He shrugged. 'They insisted it should be a splendid funeral. All the best. The flowers to remain on the grave. Campo Sperano Cemetery, of course. The new part.'

'He wasn't buried here,' Pugh said. 'His coffin went on a train to Rome.'

Cirri stopped dead, frowning, then the nervous smile returned. 'Of course. I am confusing him with the other one that day. That's right. They took him to be buried with his wife in Rome. That's what they said. I made him a splendid coffin so that the Romans wouldn't look down on us here in Naples.'

'It was a big one. But he was only a small man. Why did you make a big coffin?'

'It couldn't have been too big, Signore. Or he would have rattled round inside.'

222

'Did you put him in the coffin?'

'No. The relatives did it. They said they wished to. To show reverence and respect for a much-loved relation. They didn't want it done by someone who didn't know him.'

'Did the coffin remain in his home for the night?'

'Yes. They remained with it. They were afraid someone might break in and steal it, you understand. It's not unknown. Coffins are expensive. They also said they wished to pray. They wanted candles and prayers and a priest, they said.'

'There was no priest. No candles. No prayers. Why did you make such a big coffin?'

'It was not too big, Signore,' Cirri insisted.

'Did you measure him?'

'They measured him. They said they had a cousin who'd been in the business and they didn't want strangers there. They were very certain about it. Full of respect for the dead. Wouldn't let me near him. They were so insistent, in fact, I wondered if he'd died of something odd – typhoid or cholera. That sort of thing. It's not unknown when it grows warm. They asked for the coffin to be made for a big man.'

'You saw him in the coffin?'

'It fitted him well.'

'With all the padding?'

'Yes.'

'Of which there was a lot?'

'They asked that he should be comfortable.'

'Then what happened?'

'Signore?'

'It stayed the night in the house with these men who paid you cash and said they were relatives. But you didn't take it to the station for the Rome train.'

'No, Signore. I sublet the funeral. I had other work and it was a simple carrying job.'

Pugh wondered if the truth was that Cirri had been nervous of the transaction and the men who were conducting it, and had been trying to avoid being too

223

involved. 'Who hired the uncle from Rome?'

'The uncle from Rome?'

'There *was* one. With a car with a Roman number plate and a medal ribbon.'

Cirri looked blank. 'I saw no uncle from Rome,' he said.

Pugh frowned. 'They wanted six attendants,' he said. 'Why?'

'They thought the coffin would be heavy.'

'He was a small man.' Pugh plugged the fact again, and once more Cirri stuck to his original description.

'There was a lot of padding.'

'Made of what? Lead?'

They were getting nowhere.

Pugh left Cirri nervously discussing a new coffin with the old man and the boy. He had checked the agencies who provided the well-dressed men who gave distinction to humble funerals. They were all situated in the poorer part of the city, so he left his motor bike behind and walked.

The Agenzia Gesmundo was in a shabby little shop in the Via Ingrao, and the owner, one Gino Gesmundo, was a small, thin man wearing a pair of pince-nez with a cracked lens and a nose piece which appeared to have been repaired with sticking plaster stolen from an army hospital. He knew nothing of the Grei funeral. 'Not us, Signore,' he said. 'We have some splendid relations, of course. They speak the Roman dialect, the Roman accent, and they do not use their hands.' He opened a drawer and produced a medal with a pink ribbon. 'The Legion of Honour, Signore. We have acquired it for them to wear. The car we hire, but we have a Roman number plate. It is little trouble to change it. Of course, now that Rome's been liberated we can arrange for them to be picked up at the station as if they've arrived by train!' He smiled. 'If the Signore Sergente should wish a relative to impress the neighbours or, perhaps, a

224

young lady to while away an evening' – Gesmundo's smile widened – 'with no questions asked, of course.'

There were two other similar agencies offering everything under the sun – the usual 'uncles', wealthy 'relatives' or pretty 'cousins', to say nothing of young girls, even young boys – but neither of them knew anything of Grei.

'He couldn't have been important,' one of them said.

Pugh took his thoughts to Jones, who was still pondering the question of the Detto Banti canvasses. As soon as Pugh appeared, he lifted his head.

'I've just heard Baracca's due to be posted home,' he said. 'And that he's negotiating a lift in a Dakota to London. You can bet that if we turn those paintings over, they'll go with him to the States.'

Pugh was showing no interest and Jones was faintly irritated. 'What's the matter with you?' he said. 'I thought this was your baby.'

'I've got another one,' Pugh said. 'I believe they're twins.'

He explained what he'd been thinking and Jones leaned forward, his eyes gleaming.

'Probably just someone earning a little on the side,' he said. 'All the Italians do it, and this uncle from Rome's an old dodge.'

'This one wasn't the right type. There was the usual medal ribbon and the car had a Roman number plate, but he was a phoney, all the same.'

'All the uncles from Rome are phoneys. We know that.'

'This one wasn't even a phoney uncle from Rome. He was a *phoney* phoney uncle from Rome. He was impressive. He was well-dressed but he wasn't the right type. Uncles from Rome are chosen because they speak in a Roman accent and because they don't use their hands when they talk. This one was Vicenzo Sansovino and the last time I saw him he was Mayor of Vicinamontane, and he was offering veiled threats that

225

if I didn't turn over the Detto Banti canvasses it might be worse for me. He's no uncle from Rome. He uses his hands and speaks in a Neapolitan accent. He'd never be accepted. I know, because I've heard him speak. He's also in touch with Tirandolo, my drug-pushing friend. He's one of Vito Genovese's boys, and I suspect that, since he couldn't get his mitts on the Detto Banti canvasses, he's been put on to something else.'

Jones was looking puzzled. 'So what are you getting at?'

'There was something special about that bloody funeral,' Pugh said.

'What sort of special?'

'I don't know, but if this Grei family wanted to see an uncle from Rome at the funeral, why have him accompany the coffin to Rome? Why not produce someone in Rome itself and have him meet the coffin there? And why bother, anyway? According to old Mori, they're a wealthy family, and wealthy families don't bother with an uncle from Rome. It's the lower middle classes who want to impress. If they're wealthy they don't need to. But I don't think Grei *was* from a wealthy family. I think he was just a dead man who was reported to the police, and that someone at the *Questura* who knew what was wanted reported the fact to where it mattered. He was grabbed because someone wanted a spare stiff.' Pugh thought for a moment. 'Besides,' he went on, 'I looked up the agencies who supply the uncles and they know nothing about the Grei funeral. Nobody asked any of *them* to supply an uncle.'

Jones frowned, and Pugh pressed his point. 'On one of the first trains to Rome,' he went on. 'Remember that.'

Jones frown grew deeper. 'In Reggio di Calabria,' he said, 'they think that now the Germans have been pushed north, drugs from Africa are going to arrive in larger quantities because there's going to be more of Italy where they can be disposed of. And I've just heard that Rome's reporting dud penicillin there.' He lit a cigarette and drew on it thoughtfully. 'But since they've not had time to start a racket up there yet, it must be going up from Naples.' He looked up. 'That coffin would go as goods, and you have to get special permission to remove goods northwards. So where did they get it? Who gave it? Find out.'

It didn't take Pugh long. The despatch form was there in the office at the station and the clerk indicated the official stamp at the bottom. It was smudged, as if it had been smudged deliberately, and it was worn, the letters broken, but it clearly showed the US army's eagle.

When he returned with the form, Jones stared at it and listened with increasing interest to what he had to offer. 'US army?' he said. 'Then the original must have been signed either by some clerk at their headquarters who's mixed up in a racket and was providing a false signature, or by an American officer who won't be queried.'

'Of the rank of major or above,' Pugh said. 'That's the regulation.'

'The next rank above major,' Jones ended pointedly, 'is colonel.'

They lifted their heads and stared at each other for a long time.

'I think,' Pugh said, 'that it's time one of us went to Rome.'

The condition of the Eternal City was much the same as that of its more profane little brother, Naples, and it could barely contain its air of excitement. For the final defence of the place, German soldiers had been hauled out of hospital and formed into a last-ditch battalion, but the forces against them had been too much. The Gruppa Azione Patriottica, a Communist action group of terrorists, had been eliminating spies, collaborationists, soldiers or anybody they disliked for some time, cutting telephone wires, putting spikes down on the road and setting off bombs.

But now the Germans were gone and for the first time in twenty-two years people were discussing their politics openly in the cafés and bars with the same delirious feeling of freedom that was just beginning to wear off in Naples. They had spent too long staring hunger in the face, listening to screams in the night, the spatter of machine guns and the hurried clomp of nailed boots. Now the shutters, which had remained firmly closed against everything, were being opened at last, Jews were appearing from their hiding places – one had been sleeping for months inside an altar – and there were escaped British and American prisoners of war openly in the streets. There were also escaped Russians, huge hairy creatures who had been living wild, terrifying the peasants and beggaring them with their enormous appetites, and people of all political persuasions who had tried to withstand the Germans and the Fascists throughout the occupation.

But already prices had started to soar, and gas and

water were still cut off and, though it was possible to eat in restaurants, the food came from the black market and only the rich were able to afford it, usually by selling their possessions, even their bed linen, in the street. But, despite the grisly stories of torture in the Via Tasso, where the Gestapo had had its headquarters, there was still some of the good Roman ostentation of bowing and hand-kissing, and still a little nostalgic Italian sniggering at the few impertinent gestures of defiance they had got away with.

The British had appeared only in small numbers. The American Commander of the 5th Army and his horde of newsmen and cameramen had occupied most of the attention since the liberation, and there had even been some attempts to keep the British out so that it would be an entirely American liberation, but a few had made it and there was a defiant sign chalked on a wall, '*Gli inglesi stanno a Roma*' – The British have arrived in Rome. On the other hand, just below, there was another sign: 'We do not want Germans, Americans *or* English. Let us weep in peace.'

There were a few grumbles that the Pope had done nothing to help Italy during the occupation, but most people accepted that he had been in exactly the same powerless position as themselves. The day before Pugh arrived, the Pontiff had agreed to meet the Allied press and, with times changing, the women correspondents had not gone to the interview in black veils and dresses but had been in pants and forage caps, and throughout the interview there had been flashing lights and cries of 'Hold it, Pope!' and 'Attaboy!' and 'Gee, that's great!' The Pope had not enjoyed himself.

By now, though, the excitement was beginning to die down a little and things were becoming normal, whereas only a few days before, the mobs had been in the streets, shooting the informers who had given away people who had hidden Italian soldiers. The director of the Regina Coeli prison, where so many political prisoners and deportees had been kept, had been lynched. Identified by wives and mothers of men who had suffered under the Nazi-Fascist control as the personification of collaboration, he had been spotted by a crowd who were actually screaming for the blood of someone else entirely, trampled on, dragged half-naked in front of a tram – the driver of which had refused to run his vehicle over him – and finally thrown into the Tiber, where youths had beaten him to death with oars. With his body finally hanging from the bars of a window of his own prison, it had emerged that, far from collaborating, he had in fact been trying to save lives and had been in contact with the Jews and the Committee of National Liberation, a clandestine organisation set up against the Germans.

Like Naples station, Rome station was crowded with people trying to find relatives from whom they had been cut off for months, and here and there about the streets were flowers and little shrines on still blood-stained pavements, where people had been shot. When partisan bombs had blown up a lot of Germans in the Via Pasala, the Germans had gone berserk with revolvers and machine guns; terrified children had run in circles until they had collapsed, and nervous people had crowded on to the trams which circled the city, and remained there for over an hour, going round and round until they felt it safe to descend.

The air was still thick with resentment and vengeance, and the station staff, struggling against the increasing numbers trying to travel now that it was possible, were in no mood to help Pugh. The office where all the paperwork was done was undermanned and being run by a few tired clerks.

'As if we haven't enough to do just trying to get the trains running again,' one of them said, staring sullenly at Pugh's uniform.

He didn't offer much hope of finding out what had

been carried on trains from Naples but, as it happened and obviously to his surprise, he managed to unearth the sheet which showed Grei's coffin as 'goods' in the guard's van.

'*Cassa da morto*,' he read. '*Una. Cadavere: Uno. Al interno.* Coffin: One. Corpse: One. Inside.'

'Name?'

'You also expect a name, Signore?' The clerk waxed sarcastic. 'It is Grei, Gustavo.'

'Who gave permission for the coffin to be transported?'

'I have it here.' The clerk stared at the illegible signature. 'Someone who wishes to remain anonymous, it seems; but the rank is clear – Tenente Colonello. Lieutenant-colonel. The name could be anything, including Jesus, or Joseph or even Mary, Mother of God.'

'Where did the coffin go?'

'Signore, I don't have eyes everywhere. I didn't see it go. I'm just a clerk. You must ask a porter. Or perhaps a guard, who would have required a signature and possibly an address to release it. With a coffin containing a corpse, they would not be required to come here.' The clerk grinned suddenly. 'The delay here could be so long, putrefaction could set in.'

It didn't take long to find a porter who remembered the coffin. He and his workmate had brought up a trolley to carry the flowers.

'*I fiore!*' he said ecstatically. 'The flowers! One fell off and I took it home to my wife. It is still in a glass on the table.'

'What about the coffin? Who carried that? Some other porters?'

The porter turned a shocked look at Pugh. 'A coffin, Signore? Containing a corpse? The undertakers took it. There were six attendants waiting on the platform for it. And a two-horse hearse. Such splendid plumes.'

'What about the relatives? Did they meet it?'

'They accompanied, Signore. From Naples. Three splendidly dressed men. Such coats and hats! Such wealth! They gave me a thousand lire tip! Just for carrying the flowers. No weight at all.'

'Three of them?'

'Three of them, Signore. One very important. He wore a medal ribbon. Two less important. A captain and his lieutenants, you might say.'

You might well, Pugh thought.

'What about where the coffin went to? Did you hear the address?'

'Not me, Signore. I was only the porter. On the other hand' – the porter tapped his nose – 'I remember now—'

'You *did* hear an address?'

'No, Signore, I didn't. But I did see the name of the undertaker as we were putting the flowers round the coffin in the hearse. A splendid hearse, Signore. The sort I would like for myself. Such well-fed horses. The name was Andreotti and it came from the Via Moroni. Doubtless, the Signore Sergente could verify.'

He could indeed. 'You're sure of the name?'

'I saw it clearly, Signore. Very clearly. Right under my nose. And my eyes are good.'

'Thanks.' Determined not to be outdone by Genovese's boys, Pugh offered a thousand-lire note and the porter slammed to attention and saluted.

'It is good to have the British in Rome, Signore,' he said. 'They stole the piano from our canteen for a sergeants' mess. But the Germans shot our dog. The British would never shoot a dog.'

The clerk in the office regarded Pugh's return with a sigh. 'Telephone book,' Pugh demanded.

The name of Andreotti, Piero, agente di pompe funebri, was there. Via Moroni, 19.

The Via Moroni was in the north of the city, not far from the station and close to the railway line. It was an area of flat-fronted blocks interspersed here and there with open yards, some of which had been made from bombed areas. Pompe Funebri Andreotti occupied a yard behind a high, spiked gate and was fronted by a small shop whose glass had been painted black.

The owner, whom Pugh took to be Piero Andreotti, was wary and preferred to talk of irrelevant details.

'We used our best horses,' he said. 'Mefistofele – a strange name for a horse used by an undertaker, I think – and Massaniello. Very reliable animals. Never disturbed by traffic. Not even by bicycles; there are a great many bicycles in Rome these days, and the young don't hesitate to ride under their noses. You can imagine what would happen if the horses took fright. *Che disastro!* The hearse is our best. It was insisted on. We have two, of course. Most undertakers have only one. It has rubber tyres. Very silent. Very distinguished. The other is for lesser occasions. Second-class – but still very dignified, of course.'

'Where did it go?' Pugh demanded bluntly.

'Where?'

'The coffin. It isn't still here, is it?'

'But, no, Signore! I understand the poor soul died five days ago. It would be most unwise in the growing heat to keep it that long. It went to the Cimitero Monumentale.'

'Immediately?'

'No, Signore. They said they wanted it taken to the home of the relatives.'

'Who said so?'

'The signori who accompanied it. Very fine gentlemen they were, too. They said they wished for candles and prayers and a priest.'

'The undertaker in Naples said they had candles and prayers and a priest there. Why did they want them again?'

'For the Roman relatives, Signore? I understand Gustavo Grei was a relation who had died in Naples after being cut off by the war. He was being brought back by cousins to his family in Rome.'

'Where do these cousins live?'

'Via Romolo e Remo. I have the address here. *Numero* 31.'

'And the family?'

The undertaker stared at his book. 'Name of Focchia. Emmanuele Focchia. I always look up names and addresses for safety. There are too many crooks about. They were expecting it. The coffin was carried up the stairs to the living room, where it remained overnight. The next morning we collected it and removed it to the Cimitero Monumentale.'

'Smell the candles?'

'Signore?'

'You can smell candles when they've been burning. For a lying-in-state, for instance. Probably even incense, if the priest came and brought an altar boy or a server.'

Andreotti suddenly looked worried. 'I smelled neither candles nor incense, Signore.'

'They didn't in Naples either. Did you open the coffin for them and close it the following day?'

'They said they wished to do it themselves.'

'Did you see any sign that they had?'

'I didn't look, Signore.'

'What about the coffin? Did you notice anything odd about it?'

'Odd, Signore? Nothing except that it was a big one. For a large man. The man inside must have been very big and overweight.'

'He was a small man. Your size.'

Andreotti looked puzzled then he smiled. 'He must have rattled round inside, Signore.' He frowned. 'But when we were carrying it up I discerned no movement. Perhaps they packed it with his treasures. They do sometimes. The Neapolitans are superstitious – barbaric, like the ancient Egyptians. But who am I to argue? They paid me well.'

'In cash?'

'A great deal. More than I asked. So that I would do things exactly as they requested.'

'Did you arrange for an uncle from Rome to be with the coffin?'

Andreotti sniffed. 'That's a Neapolitan practice. We're more civilised up here.'

Pugh frowned. 'What about the coffin? Did it seem the same when you brought it down as it did when you took it up?'

'But, of course, Signore.' Andreotti stopped dead and slapped his forehead. 'Since you mention it, Signore, I don't think it did.'

'In what way was it different?'

'Well, I didn't think about it, of course, at the time. I was concerned only with getting it down without dropping it. But it was easier than I'd expected, and I noticed that the body moved. You can tell, Signore, when you have it on your shoulder and your ear to the wood. I felt it move. I heard it move.'

'But it didn't move as you took it up?'

'No, Signore. And it was heavy.'

'It was a big coffin.'

'A very big coffin. We have a stock of caskets for the deceased – all normal sizes, but I've never come across one this size before. That's very odd, isn't it?'

'Yes,' Pugh agreed. 'Very odd. The men who had brought the coffin from Naples: did they attend the funeral?'

'No, Signore. They had a big car which waited in the street. They followed the hearse for a little way but then they turned off.'

'And the relations in Rome?'

Andreotti looked puzzled. 'They didn't attend either, Signore. The men said they weren't well and that only they would be going. But they didn't, as I say. In the end there was just the priest, myself, the bearers and the director of the cemetery. I feel a man should never be sent to his Maker without someone to see him go.'

'Do you have the names of the men who hired you?'
Andreotti shrugged.
'Didn't you present them with a bill?'
'They insisted there should be no bill. They gave me no names. Just cash. I didn't argue. One doesn't under such circumstances – especially these days.'

The Via Romolo e Remo was not far away, in a district of tall flat-faced buildings containing apartments, not unlike the building where Gustavo Grei had died in Naples. Emmanuele Focchia belonged to the same class. He was a clerk and, though he was working, he was clearly not paid enough. Both he and his wife were thin and hollow-eyed and looked as though they hadn't had enough to eat for ages. He opened the door nervously, and when Pugh mentioned Gustavo Grei he saw Focchia flinch.

The apartment was small and as ugly as the building. A new lamp and a new radio standing on a table seemed quite out of keeping with the general shabbiness of the rest of the place.

When Pugh explained why he was there, Focchia and his wife exchanged nervous glances.

'Your uncle,' Pugh said. 'Arnaldo Grei.'

'That's right,' Focchia agreed. 'Uncle Arnaldo.'

'Of Via Opera, 19, Naples.'

'That's right.'

'Your father's brother, or your wife's father's brother?'

'Why do you ask, Signore?'

'Documents get a bit mixed up. The coffin was brought here from Naples, wasn't it?'

'Yes.'

'By relatives?'

'Yes.'

'Names?'

Focchia gave a frantic glance at his wife. 'Well—'

Pugh pulled out a notebook and waited as if to write down the names.

Focchia gave his wife another desperate glance. 'Well—' he said again. 'Well, you see, they were not close relations of mine, you understand. They were *his* relations.'

'So why did they bring the body to Rome?'

'Well – ah! – because he had left a request that he should be buried in Rome with his wife.'

'What about his children?'

'They are in the north. At the other side of the front line.'

'Did *you* request that the body be brought north?'

'Yes. I knew of his wish, you see.'

'Whom did you contact in Naples?'

'An undertaker.'

'Name?'

'I don't have the name.' Focchia's answers were coming more easily now as he gained confidence.

'So how did you pay his bill?'

'I didn't pay the bill. The Naples relations did that. The relations who brought the body here.'

'I saw the coffin. It was a big one. He must have been a big man.'

'Yes. A big man. Very strong when he was young.'

'What about the undertaker here in Rome?'

'Ah – well, you see – that had all been arranged—'

'But not by you?'

'No. Not by me. By the relatives from Naples.'

'What about the burial? Where was it?'

'I regret I didn't attend it.'

'Why not?'

'My wife was unwell.'

'But, of course, you met the coffin when it arrived at the station?'

'Yes.' Focchia caught a despairing warning glance from his wife and changed his mind. 'No! No, of course not! I forgot. I told you. My wife was unwell.'

Pugh put the notebook and pen away and looked at Focchia. 'You're telling me a pack of lies, aren't you?'

'No, your honour. I swear on the shroud of my sister

237

who died as pure as driven snow at the age of seventeen.'

'Save your breath,' Pugh said, not unkindly. 'I know more about your uncle than you do.'

Focchia smiled. 'That's possible, your honour.'

'His name wasn't Arnaldo. It was Gustavo. And he didn't live in the Via Opera. His address was Via Maddalena, 7. And he didn't have a wife buried here because he didn't have a wife, or any children, in the north or anywhere else. He was a bachelor.'

Focchia looked panic-stricken. 'Well, you see, he wasn't a close relative.'

'How close do you want him? He was your uncle, you said.'

'Well—'

'You don't know the undertaker in Naples because the funeral was nothing to do with you. Neither there nor here. And you didn't attend the funeral – which incidentally was at the Cimitero Monumentale – because you were never asked.' Pugh smiled. 'And this uncle of yours whose name and address you don't know, whose funeral you didn't attend – despite the fact that the coffin rested in your house for a night – was not a tall, strong man. He was small. Your size. I think you'd better tell me what you know.'

Focchia gave an agonised glance at his wife, who promptly burst into tears and flopped into a chair alongside the new radio.

'It was nothing to do with me,' Focchia muttered.

Pugh's voice grew harsher. 'The coffin was here! In your house! For a whole night!'

'Yes.' Focchia seemed able to admit that without worry.

'He wasn't your uncle, was he?!'

'He was – well – a relation.'

'What relation? I can check.'

'I—' Focchia flung another despairing glance at his wife and gave up the struggle. 'No,' he admitted. 'He was not my relation.'

238

'So why did the coffin come here?'

'I was paid to keep it here for the night.'

'I won't ask how much. I expect it was enough.'

'It was substantial, your honour,' Focchia agreed. 'We were in need of it. It seemed very little to do for the money that was offered.'

'Who gave you this money?'

Focchia's eyes were frantic again. 'I can't tell you.'

'Why? Because you're afraid of him?'

'I' – Focchia shook his head as though recovering from a blow – 'yes, your honour, I am afraid.'

'Was the coffin opened here?'

'I didn't see it opened.'

'So what happened exactly?'

'I was told to tell the neighbours that my uncle in Naples had died and that now the trains were running he was being brought to Rome to be alongside his wife.'

'Go on.'

'We were told to expect the coffin on the morning train from Naples. We were not to meet it. We had simply to wait in the apartment, dressed in our best clothes, with black armbands, because it was being brought by relations.'

'What happened when it arrived?'

'We met it by the main entrance and followed it up the stairs. When it was inside the apartment, one of the men who brought it closed the door. Then he gave me a lot of money – 10,000 lire, your honour; that is a lot of money to us – and told us to go to the bedroom and stay there. After it was dark, we were told to leave the building and stay away for the night. We went to my daughter's house, which is at Frascati. We said there was a gas leak.'

'When did you come back?'

'When they told us to come back. The next morning.'

'What then?'

'The coffin was still here, but there were several suitcases in the entrance. Shortly afterwards the undertaker arrived and took the coffin away. The men

239

stood with their hats against their chests, and followed it down the stairs.'

'And you?'

'We were told to stay here and to say my wife was unwell and couldn't go to the funeral.'

'What happened to the suitcases?'

'The men took them. They put them in a big black car which arrived to take them to the cemetery.'

'Would it surprise you to know that those men didn't go to the cemetery, either?'

Focchia sighed. 'No, your honour. It would not surprise me.'

'What about when the coffin had gone? What did you do?'

'We tidied the apartment. Chairs were not in their proper places, of course. The coffin had rested on four of them in the living room. We put them back where they belonged.'

'Did you find anything? Did the men leave anything behind?'

'Wrappings, your honour. That's all.'

'What sort of wrappings?'

Focchia glanced at his wife, who dried her tears and disappeared to the kitchen. She returned later with an armful of paper.

'We thought for safety we had better get rid of it in small portions,' Focchia explained. 'A little at a time.'

Pugh sifted through the paper. Eventually, he found a label marked 'United States Army. 95th Evacuation Hospital.'

'Is this all?'

'There was a cracked bottle. We kept it in case it was wanted.'

'Bring it.'

The bottle was small and Pugh guessed it had contained drugs of some sort.

'Anything else?'

'No, Signore.'

'What do *you* think was in the coffin? Besides the body.'

Focchia shrugged. 'I don't know, Signore,' he said. 'I don't know if there was anything. But I smelled whisky.'

8

It was while he was in Frascati checking Focchia's story
with his daughter that Pugh heard the Allies in France
were on the move and, since the invasion of France
seemed to herald the approaching end of the war more
than anything in Italy ever had, he decided it might be a
good idea to go on to Severino Campagna and pick up
the paintings he had stored when he had departed for
England early in 1940.

Signora Foa was pleased to see him. She looked older
and very thin, but she insisted on producing a bottle of
vermouth and left it with him while she searched for the
canvasses. When he looked at them his heart sank. He
had thought they were good but now, after four years,
he recognised how awful they were. Perhaps, as he'd
suggested to Tamara, he ought to go back to law
because he'd never make a living as a painter.

'They are very beautiful,' the old lady said.

'If you want them,' Pugh said, 'they're yours. They're
not very good, but you ought to be able to sell them for a
little. It'll compensate you for looking after them for so
long.'

He was glad to turn his back on that part of his life
because, he saw now, it had been lonely, disillusioned
and wasted, and he was glad to report back to Jones.

'I think we've got to open that grave,' he said.

Jones rubbed his nose. 'What are you expecting to
find?' he asked.

'Nothing,' Pugh said. 'Except a small man in a very
large coffin which will doubtless be weighted with
stones wrapped in blankets to stop them moving about.

They were in a hurry and thought they could get away with it, and they couldn't be bothered to put on a show of going to the burial. They wanted to get away with the loot.'

'What do you think it was?'

'Surgical instruments? Drugs? Penicillin? I think there was whisky, too, because they opened a bottle in the Focchias' apartment.'

'Who do you reckon's behind it?'

'The usual lot. But Sansovino, who was the *sindaco* at Vicinamontane, was one of the men who took the coffin to Rome. He's the chap I saw visiting Tirandolo at Poggio Reale after I shoved him in clink for pinching penicillin. Perhaps he's taken the operation over from him while he's hors de combat. The other two were men I saw with him at Vicinamontane. I think they're opening a new route. That stuff you were talking about in Reggio di Calabria isn't all going by sea. Some of it's going by rail from here.'

'Right,' Jones nodded. 'I'll have a word with the investigation department of the military police. They'll back us up. How much do you think military personnel are involved?'

'They must be involved somewhere. How else would they get the drugs?'

'Do we have anything else that will convince them?'

'I wondered who it was who approached Focchia to do what he did, so I tried to find out something about him. He's a clerk at a garage. A big one. Name of Riparazione Partenope. Then I wondered why they'd picked *him* in particular, because the gangs never use people who're related or known to be in touch for a thing like this. It turned out he was just handy, that's all. All the same, it's interesting.'

Jones obligingly looked interested.

'Riparazione Partenope,' Pugh went on, 'is part of Industriale Pugliese, which seems to be a front operation for a man called Eugenio Gerratana, who's

well known to the Rome police. He was a collaboration-
ist with the Germans, with the Fascists, with a lot of
people, but he's powerful enough to be untouchable.
He's the Roman equivalent to Vito Genovese. He runs
the gangs. The big gangs are his and the little gangs pay
him a toll to be allowed to operate. There's one other
thing. His wife's name was Raffaela Tirandolo. Tirandolo's Gerratana's brother-in-law.'

Jones grinned. 'Is he, by God? That's interesting.
We're going to have to work this one carefully.'

'Very carefully. Gerratana's got a lot of pull and he
lives as if he knows it – in a big house near the Sastavera
Gardens – and he doesn't give a damn about the police.'

'He will if we find anything on his property. Because if
this thing links up, we might round up a few others here
and there as well. Perhaps not him or Genovese, but if
we can round up enough of their sidekicks, we can stop
their antics.' Jones frowned. 'For a time, anyway, until
they train some new blood. Still, even that would be a
triumph. Let's get on with it.' He paused. 'But let's play
our cards close to our chest, shall we? This is between
you and me and the general. We don't want anything
leaking out.'

'What about Tasker? He's supposed to know what
we're doing.'

'I think Baracca might be involved in this as well as in
trying to get the Detto Bantis out of the country. The
bastard might even be another of Gerratana's relations,
so we'll keep it from Tasker, just in case he lets
something drop.'

It wasn't easy to get permission for the disinterment of
Gustavo Grei without letting everybody in the world
know what they were up to. But the colonel in command
of the special investigation branch of the military police
was an ex-Scotland Yard man, and he wasn't the type to
back away from responsibility. All he requested was
that one of his men whom he could trust – 'And, by

244

God,' he admitted, 'you can't trust 'em all' – should be present. He signed the necessary forms without argument, and Pugh and Jones and a police major set off for Rome by road.

Highway 6 was still crammed with military vehicles going north, and all along the road were smashed hamlets and small towns, now lit by the sunshine that showed their wounds. The area was trying desperately to claw itself back to a normal existence in a waste of destroyed buildings and devastated fields and vineyards. Heavy carts dragged by lean oxen held up the traffic, and here and there peasants and monks worked to make ruined buildings habitable. The roads were full of refugees; men, women and children struggling along with all they possessed – bedding, mattresses, clothes and household goods carried on their backs or piled on handcarts. The desolation was everywhere, and in small dark rooms whole families crouched round a single table, indifferent to the moving troops and vehicles, to the shattered buildings and the debris of the battles.

Cassino, where the road looped south round the mountain, was in ruins and above their heads, brooding, lay the slopes that had dominated the battlefield for so long. There was a titanic majesty about the area, frightening in its vastness, and on one peak was the crumbled shape of what had been the sixth century Benedictine Abbey of Monte Cassino until a massive air attack had been made on it earlier in the year.

Rome had the look now of a sick individual who was gradually recovering strength. It was on its feet at last, shaky and weak, but moving. What business there was, was operating, and those who had jobs were going with certainty about their work. There were soldiers everywhere, mostly Americans but a few British, too, and as they passed through the Piazza Venezia they heard bagpipes.

They had not informed the American authorities of their visit and were operating solely with the British military police. The major in command was worried because there were a lot of revenge shootings of collaborators by people who had lost relatives under the occupation, and a great deal of partisan activity just to the north. Strafed continually by Allied aircraft, the Germans had unleashed their fury on the partisans who had tried to ambush them, and it had been reciprocated. Both Germans and partisans had been shot and tortured, and the Germans were having to form specialist units to combat the attacks.

But the police major had laid on help and went with them to the civic authorities and to the director of the cemetery, who led them to the grave. Over it already lay a marble slab, large and heavy and lacking in interest.

'Bit quick, wasn't it?' Pugh said. 'I didn't think they worked as fast as that.'

'It appeared two days after the burial,' the director said. 'I was surprised, because marble coverings take time.'

'It's square,' the policeman pointed out in a flat voice. 'Unsculptured, and has only the single name, Grei, which is not a long one. There are no forenames, no dates. Four letters. It wouldn't take long.'

The director gave them the address of the stone-mason who had provided the stone. He said he knew nothing more than that he had been paid – in cash – to carve the name on the block of marble and put it in place.

'At once, they said,' he told them.

'Who were "they"?'

The stonemason shrugged. 'I don't know, Signore. They gave me no names. Just instructions – and money.'

His description indicated the same three men who had hired the clerk, Focchia; together with Andreotti, the funeral director; and Cirri, in Naples. Obviously their influence and interests were wide enough to cover both cities.

'And probably a lot in between as well,' Jones said.

*

The following morning, before it was properly light, Jones and Pugh and the police major appeared at the cemetery, where the director was waiting for them. He led them down the rutted gravel-covered road to the new part of the cemetery, where Grei was buried. Fresh gravel had not been laid on it since the war and it was uneven, bare in parts and green with sprouting grass. The director had erected canvas screens round the grave. 'For a measure of privacy,' he said. 'There won't be anyone here at this time but we have to preserve the decencies.' And just alongside was a mobile crane belonging to the Royal Engineers. The Engineers had already managed to pass wire slings under the stone and the ends were shackled to the hook of the crane.

To one side, looking faintly embarrassed, like poor relations at a rich man's party, were the two grave-diggers the director of the cemetery had supplied. They were elderly Italians in shabby clothes, their faces gaunt as if they could do with a good meal, their chins sprouting beards several days old. Standing with them was a young doctor from the RAMC, who looked as if he hadn't the slightest idea what was going on, and a priest, whom the director of the cemetery had insisted should be present.

'Believe me,' the police major said, 'this has taken some doing without the Americans finding out.'

'Perhaps it's as well they haven't,' Jones said. 'If – as we suspect – one of their people's involved, there might be an attempt at a cover-up.'

The major nodded to the Engineer sergeant, and the driver of the crane started the engine. As he began to work levers and the wires tightened, the priest began to mutter to himself. The slings tautened and slowly the heavy slab of marble lifted. As it was moved to one side and laid on the ground, the priest crossed himself and the two gravediggers moved forward.

It was full daylight before they uncovered the lid of the coffin, then the two gravediggers lifted their heads to find out what to do next.

247

'Just clear the earth away,' Jones said. 'So we can lift the lid. I want to see what's inside.'

'Gustavo Grei,' the policeman said. 'What else do you expect?'

As the lid was unscrewed, they all leaned foward.

'Big coffin for a little man,' Jones said.

As Pugh had expected, the corpse of Gustavo Grei, waxen-faced, sunken-cheeked, hands folded on his chest, was dwarfed by the size of the box that contained him because there was a gap at each side of the corpse which was padded by what appeared to be rolls of blanket.

'Let's have them up here,' Jones said.

The blankets were passed up and Jones unrolled them carefully, almost as if he expected them to contain dynamite. By the time they had removed the lot, the corpse seemed lost in the enormous coffin.

'There's a lot of room left when you take those things out,' the police major said.

'Room for a few things such as contraband,' Jones agreed. 'He turned to the director of the cemetery. 'We shall need this coffin. Can you arrange to transfer the body to a coffin that would fit it?'

'Try Andreotti,' Pugh suggested. 'I expect you have his address. He'd be glad of the work.'

The director nodded. 'I'll get in touch with him at once,' he said. 'What do you wish me to do? Re-inter him?'

'Why not? He's not done much except die.'

That night, they decided to call on Focchia again. The police major went with them because by this time he was beginning to grow very suspicious.

When they drew into the Via Romolo e Remo there was a small crowd of people standing outside the door of the block where the Focchias lived. Immediately, Pugh felt his heart thump.

As they climbed out of the Jeep, heads turned towards

them as though they were expected. An Italian policeman was standing in the doorway and as Pugh showed his papers they were waved inside. As he had supposed, there was another group of people on the landing outside the Focchias' apartment, and an Italian brigadier of police talking to a man with a bag who looked like a doctor.

'What's going on?' he asked.

The policeman looked at them hostilely, but his manner changed as soon as Pugh showed his papers, and he became obsequious at once.

'An accident, Signori,' he said. 'Nothing to concern you. Purely an Italian affair.'

'Has something happened to the Focchias?'

'You know them, Signore?'

'I've been speaking to them recently. What's happened?'

'Nothing to concern you, Signore.'

'Leave us to decide that,' the police major snapped, and the brigadier turned a resentful look towards him.

'They're dead,' he said. 'There is gas in the apartment. I think they decided life wasn't worth living and gave up. It wasn't hard, I suppose. *In Italia li vuole più corragio per vivere che morire.* You need more courage these days to live than to die. You can't blame them. He hadn't much of a job and I expect things were difficult.'

'Not that bloody difficult,' Pugh said. 'He had 10,000 lire in his possession two or three days ago.'

The brigadier's eyebrows lifted. 'A clerk, Signore?'

'He told me.'

The brigadier obviously didn't believe him but he offered no objection to their entering the flat. The Focchias were lying on the floor of the kitchen, their heads near the gas oven. The windows were sealed with paper stuffed into the cracks, and Pugh turned to study the door. There was an old coat lying across the entrance to the kitchen. Instead of being at an angle, as it would have been had it been laid against the door from

249

inside, and then pushed back by whoever first opened the door, it was still lying squarely across the entrance, unmoved, and it appeared to Pugh that it had been outside.

'Who found them?' he asked.

'A Signora Fossichetti from upstairs. She came down to borrow sugar and smelled gas. The door was locked so she called the concierge, who brought a key.' He indicated a small man standing against the wall, trying to keep out of sight.

Pugh pointed to the blanket. 'Where was that when you opened the door?'

'Lying along the bottom of the door, Signore,' the concierge said. 'To keep the gas in, I suppose.'

'Inside or outside?'

'Inside, I suppose.' The concierge frowned. 'But, no, I remember now. It was outside.'

'So if they were busy committing suicide inside, who put that outside?'

The concierge shrugged and the police brigadier shouldered his way forward. 'A friend?' he suggested indifferently. 'A relation? It happens all the time. Italy's a difficult place to stay alive in these days. The incidence of suicide is high. People get help, you know.'

The police major looked at him, his face cynical. 'You, my friend,' he said sharply, 'do not have much of a future as a detective.'

9

Pugh was still in a sour mood after the incidents in Rome. He was beginning to grow angry, his mind full of the rottenness of war, which didn't consist just of men trying to kill each other. It also brought about every other kind of horror attendant on the killing – corruption, atrocities, criminality – with the strong and the wealthy living off the weak.

His temper wasn't improved when, as he was riding the motor cycle down the steep slopes from the Vomero, and enjoying the speed, the brakes failed and he ended up in the front room of a small restaurant. A few chickens, which were in there after the crumbs, disappeared through the window with a scattering of feathers amid screams and shouts of rage. Fortunately it was too early for customers and nobody was hurt, and the owner was more than compensated by the handsome sum Pugh gave him. He summoned a lorry and took the bike back to Motor Transport to tear a few strips off the indignant fitters for the failure.

Returning to the office, he and Jones tried to decide what they should do next. They were clearly not going to get very far with the deaths of the Focchias. Quite obviously they had been killed to keep them quiet, but, by the grace of God, they had a lead now to who was involved. Sansovino and his henchmen would obviously need to be questioned, but enquiries showed that Sansovino had disappeared.

'There's no doubt about it,' Jones said. 'The gangs are getting a helping hand from someone on our side of the fence.'

It was his view that it might be worth bringing in Cirri, the undertaker, who probably knew more about who was involved than he was prepared to admit. Pugh suggested they wait.

'If we pull him in, they'll bolt,' he said. 'Let's get a cast-iron case and bring the lot in all at once. We can pick up Cirri when we've got the others.'

They spent the day working out a plan of campaign. The other sergeants were called in, in case they had anything to add, but – apart from Sergeant O'Mara, who was a placid, easygoing man – they took the opportunity instead to complain about the amount of work they were having to do since the disappearance of Sergeant Waddilove.

When Pugh returned to his own office, there was a note from Tamara on the desk. It was typed – even the signature – and asked him to call and see her.

Suspecting someone had tried to contact her about the Detto Banti canvasses, he decided to go at once. She was probably wondering what had happened to him. Due to the Grei development, they had not been in touch with each other for over a week, apart from a short note clearly showing her anxiety, which asked how he was and ended 'Baci, Tamara' – Kisses, Tamara – something he found surprisingly moving. As a result he had tried twice, in between the trips to Rome, to telephone her at the hospital, but on both occasions she had not been available.

The motor bike had been repaired and, pulling it off its stand, he headed for her apartment. There were two Italian policemen standing at the end of the street where she lived, smart in their dark uniforms and white cross-belts. One of them was a man called Zolli with whom Pugh had worked on more than one occasion, and he lifted his hand in salute as Pugh passed.

Tamara's rooms were at the top of the old apartment block and the lights seemed to have fused because the stairs were shadowed. As he reached the last landing, it was dark and he decided he ought to try and get something done about it. There were a lot of strange things going on in Naples, and a darkened landing was no place for a girl as attractive as Tamara to live.

He was still thinking about it when he became aware of a shadow coming out of the recesses of the landing. Turning to meet it, he saw the gleam of metal and had the sense to move to one side. As he did so, he felt a sharp pain in his arm and heard the tearing of cloth – and it dawned on him someone was trying to murder him.

With a yell of fright, he lashed out with all his strength and, more by luck than judgement, managed to make contact. He felt the pain across his knuckles as his fist struck bone and the shadowy figure fell back. Pugh was just about to swing away in an attempt to escape when he realised that turning his back on an assailant with a knife was about as silly a thing as he could do, and instead, he turned again to face his attacker, dragging at the weapon he wore at his belt. The explosion in the narrow confines of the landing was enough to wake the dead. The heavy bullet struck the ceiling and brought down a shower of plaster.

Deciding that arguing with a revolver as big as Pugh's wasn't worth the effort, the attacker made a dive past him. As he did so, Pugh loosed off another shot, which clattered off the wall and brought down another shower of plaster. The assailant, a big man in a dark suit, plunged down the stairs, missed his step and rolled to the bottom. Scrambling to his feet, he set off again as Pugh sent another wild shot after him, intending less to kill him than to frighten the life out of him. More plaster exploded from the wall, then the attacker vanished – just as Tamara's door was wrenched open and she appeared.

'Piu!' she said. 'What is happening?'

'Somebody was waiting for you,' Pugh panted. 'I think he had robbery in mind.'

The last clattering footsteps disappeared into the

253

street, then they heard shouts and a fusillade of shots. Pugh guessed that the policemen in the street outside had seen the figure running from the house, and assuming – reasonably safely in Naples – that criminality was afoot, had taken pot shots at the fugitive. As the echoes died, there was silence. Not a door of any of the lower apartments had opened. After the months of occupation, Neapolitans were too wary to get involved. They had spent too much time listening to running feet and shots in the dark, and knew that they usually meant murder.

'You are hurt, Piu.'

It was only as Tamara spoke that Pugh noticed there was blood on his hand. Lifting it, he saw his knuckles were badly split and he guessed he must have hit his attacker in the mouth and cut his knuckles on his teeth.

'Not there,' Tamara said. 'On your arm.'

Then Pugh realised that the blood on his hand was not merely from his knuckles but was running down his sleeve.

'What has happened?'

Pugh didn't answer because he was suddenly convinced that the accident with the motor cycle earlier in the day probably hadn't been an accident at all, and that the brakes had been tampered with. Which seemed to indicate that he was nearer to the truth than he had thought.

Tamara pushed him inside the apartment and began to pull off his battledress blouse. There was a rent in the sleeve, and as he peeled back his shirt he saw a long slash down his forearm. But for his instinctive step aside, the attacker's knife would have taken him in the chest.

Tamara was fussing round him now, tearing up an old sheet to make a bandage. She found water and bathed away the blood, then began to fasten a bandage in place.

'It is deep,' she said. 'I think it ought to be stitched. But I have sticking plaster and will pull it together and fasten it like that. It would take hours to go to the hospital and get it done. I think it will be all right.'

She looked up at him as she wound the bandage on and he saw there were tears in her eyes. 'Why were you here, Piu? Why were you on the landing in the dark?'

'Because the lights didn't appear to be working.'

'They were working when I came home. I heard someone on the stairs but I didn't go out; in Naples you don't go out. Why did you come?'

'Because you asked me to.'

She looked puzzled. 'I didn't ask you, Piu.'

He showed her the typewritten note. 'I didn't send that.' She looked worried. 'Were they after me? I have had a telephone call about the pictures.'

Pugh's head jerked up. 'Which pictures?'

'The big ones. There was no mention of the small ones.'

'Who was it?'

'There was no name. It was a woman. She said she was acting for a dealer. She had heard that several Detto Bantis had been brought to Naples and did I know where they were, because her dealer friend was anxious to see them and, if they were genuine, to make an offer?'

'What did you say?'

'I said there *had* been paintings but that they had all been stolen and as far as I knew there were none left.'

'Good girl. What happened then?'

'She just rang off. No questions. Nothing.'

She still looked upset and he made her sit down. He was under no illusions that the man who had attacked him was no ordinary burglar. Either he had been after Pugh himself because of his interest in the burial of Gustavo Grei, or because he'd found out what was hidden in Tamara's flat.

'Are the paintings still safe?'

Her eyes flicked to the trapdoor above the kitchen cupboard. 'It hasn't been disturbed,' she said. 'You will notice a piece of cotton hanging down. If it had been lifted, that would have fallen. It is a trick I learned from American detective stories.'

'Have you mentioned them to anyone?'

'You said I must not.'

'I think, under the circumstances,' he said, 'that you'd better move to my place with your possessions. There are soldiers in my building and I don't think anyone would try anything there.'

She looked startled, studying his face with a worried expression. 'For the night?' she asked.

'And tomorrow. As long as you like. Certainly until we've got the pictures identified, valued and sold. It's a crummy place and it'll look better with you around.'

She looked uncertain.

'Don't worry,' he said. 'Nobody will turn a hair. Sergeant O'Mara has a girl in his rooms. So does Sergeant Plummer, though she's not permanent.' He grinned. 'And, after all, we've slept together before.'

'Not like this, I think.'

'There's a big sofa in the living room. I can sleep on that. Just until we get things sorted out.'

She hesitated a moment longer, then she nodded. 'Thank you, Piu,' she said. 'I would like that, I think.'

They were still discussing the pros and cons of the move when there was a tap on the door. Tamara gave Pugh a frightened look. He nodded to her to go to the bedroom, and, as the door shut, he drew his revolver. To his surprise, the man outside was not another intruder, but the policeman, Zolli.

'Who called you?' Pugh asked.

The policeman looked startled. 'No one, Signore. I am investigating what has just been happening in the street.'

'It didn't happen in the street,' Pugh pointed out. 'It happened here. I was attacked on the landing.' He held up his arm to show the bandage. 'You'd better come in. We were taking no chances.'

As the policeman entered, Tamara reappeared and Zolli gave her an old-fashioned look, obviously assuming that Pugh was there for one reason only.

Pugh disillusioned him by showing him the type-written message. 'I was asked to come. Someone was waiting for me.'

The policeman nodded. 'Were you involved in an investigation, Sergeant?'

'Yes, I was. A serious one.'

Zolli frowned. 'I think you should do what we do and go about in pairs. You were obviously brought here deliberately. We saw him run from the house.'

'Did you arrest him?'

'No, Signore.'

'Why not? Too late?'

'Not exactly, Signore. He's dead. My partner shot him. We shouted at him to stop. He refused, so we fired. This is Naples, Signore.' He shrugged. 'He's in the street. We'd like you to identify him as the man who attacked you.'

Pugh glanced quickly at Tamara, then he nodded. 'I'll come down. You'd better stay here. Lock the door.'

The street was still empty and the dead man was lying face-down in the gutter. There was a bullet-hole in the back of his head.

'Who is he?'

Zolli shrugged. The second policeman, who was kneeling by the body, turned it over and began to go through the pockets.

Pugh leaned closer. 'Have you a torch?'

A torch was shone on the dead man's face and the two policemen studied it carefully.

'He looks a bad lot,' the man who was kneeling by him said. 'Nothing on him. Just this.' He held up a slip of paper. On it, obviously hurriedly scrawled, was Tamara's address, Vicolo Jaccarino, 17.

'Can I keep that?'

Zolli frowned. 'It's evidence, Sergente.'

'You can have it back. Perhaps I'll be able to produce a name for you.'

Zolli handed over the paper with a show of

reluctance. 'Is there anyone who has something against you?'

'Probably a lot of people.'

'Someone paid him to get you. They gave him the address and he was waiting for you.'

Unless he was waiting for Tamara to leave so he could enter the apartment and search for the paintings, Pugh thought. Either way, it was interesting. More interesting than it had been, in fact, because the face of the dead man, distorted by death and smeared with blood as it was, was that of one of the men he'd seen in Vicinamontane outside the Palazzo Municipale talking to the Mayor, Vicenzo Sansovino, one of the 'cousins' who'd accompanied Gustavo Grei's coffin to Rome.

10

Returning to the top apartment, Pugh found Tamara packed.

'I'm ready,' she said.

'You'll be all right,' he encouraged her. 'Take no notice of anything anyone might say about you being in my apartment. Everybody's at it. There's a bath.'

'That is something I shall enjoy. Here I have to take my baths in the kitchen standing in a bowl.'

She hadn't much – one suitcase, two brown paper parcels and a hat that looked as if it had once been worn at a wedding – but there was a reading lamp, a lot of books, an old portable typewriter, two large cartons of china which she had inherited from her foster parents, and the duffel bag containing the three small Detto Bantis. Her face was flushed and a wisp of hair, decorated with a fragment of spider's web from the trapdoor in the ceiling, fell over her nose.

Leaving the two policemen, who were still waiting for the mortuary van, to keep an eye on the place until he returned, Pugh went in search of a taxi. But it was late and, with petrol short, there were none about. Finding himself near Mori's stable, he dragged the old man out. He was more than willing to help and harnessed Fiorello to his cart. Riding in the back, they took Tamara to the Casa Calafati.

As they entered, the contessa appeared. For a change she was in a long flowered dress that looked as if it had once been the cover of a settee. She leaned limply against the wall, coughing as if about to die, and stared at Pugh through haunted black eyes.

Dragging at a cigarette, she coughed a little more before she could speak to them. 'The *ragazza* is coming to live here?'

'Yes, Contessa. With me.'

'It is against the rules. I don't make them, of course. Is she a good girl?'

'She is.'

'Sometimes I wonder if the Sergente Plummer's girl is a good girl.' She shook under a volley of coughs and gestured towards the decaying stairs. 'Very well, Sergente. I trust you. You have always behaved yourself. I am blind.'

Pushing Tamara inside his apartment and telling her to lock the door, Pugh got old Mori to take him back to where he had left the motor cycle. Driving to the Palazza Pizzoni, he found Jones's office was locked and there was no sign of any of the other sergeants.

Going to his desk, he fished among the papers for the file he'd been saddled with just before his departure north to Vicinamontane, concerning one Private Peter Charles Weeden, of the Royal West Kent Regiment. It had started, it seemed, with an enquiry into an Italian girl who was accused of having swindled an American soldier but, unfortunately, it had been discovered that the soldier wasn't American at all but a British deserter, Private Weeden, of the West Kents, who had decided that, since the Americans were better paid, better fed and better clothed, he was wasting his time in the British army. Acquiring a uniform, he had affected an American accent and claimed he belonged to an American unit. It had been his inability to leave women alone that had exposed him, and the information had been passed on to Tasker, who had passed it on to Jones, who had handed it to Sergeant O'Mara, who had passed it to Pugh. Tasker's note was still attached on the report and the original complaint was signed 'Arnold J. Baracca, Colonel,' and was stamped with his office stamp.

Looking in O'Mara's desk for a magnifying glass,

Pugh laid the slip of paper given to him by Zolli alongside. The formation of the a's and the r's and the c's was exactly the same as those in Baracca's signature. From his drawer, he produced the form with its blurred signature that had granted permission for the transportation of Gustavo Grei's body to Rome, which he had obtained from the station. Laying it alongside the note attached to the report on Private Weeden, Pugh lifted the magnifying glass again. The signature was still illegible, obviously deliberately so, but here again there were the same c's and the same r's, and the office stamp, broken and worn, was exactly the same in every detail.

Carefully locking the papers away in his drawer, he sat for a while staring into space. If the note found on the man who had attacked him had been written by Baracca, it seemed to indicate that it was Barracca who had wanted Pugh done away with. He had suspected for some time that Baracca was interested in the Detto Banti canvases, but was he also somehow involved in the business of the coffin full of drugs and whisky going to Rome? And who was the woman who had telephoned Tamara? It could only have been some girl friend of Baracca's.

But Pugh hadn't told anyone but Jones, and he felt he could trust Jones as he could trust Tamara and old Tassinari and Foscari. That left only one person who could have passed on the information that the paintings had reached Naples – Marcopolo Detto Banti.

Pugh was still frowning as he headed for his rooms. Tamara was just appearing from the bathroom when he arrived. She looked pink and happy but still not entirely certain what he was after. However, she had done a cleaning job on the little flat and a lot of clothes that had been left lying about were neatly folded and put away. She had obviously come out in a rash of womanly house-pride.

Impulsively he bent to kiss her, and she lifted her face

261

so naturally to him the familiarity startled him.

'I am happy here,' she said. 'It is a good apartment.'

'Not very big,' he admitted, 'but big enough. I'll arrange for you to have a key.'

She looked worried. 'Do you think the man will come again?'

'*He* won't. He's in the mortuary. He was shot dead. But there might be another.'

'Here?'

'Not here. There are too many soldiers here.'

'Please take care, Piu.'

'I may have to go to Rome. If I do, I'll arrange with Sergeant O'Mara to keep an eye on you. You can trust him and he won't bother you. He's got his own girl.'

He took her to the small restaurant down the road, where most of the sergeants ate. O'Mara was there with his girl and he gave Pugh a startled look that changed to admiration as he studied Tamara. They joined forces and Pugh bought wine, and they finished off with brandy. By the time they left, Pugh and Tamara were feeling warm enough to sit in the gardens along the Via Caracciolo.

'Have we found our painting expert yet?' Tamara asked.

'We've got one and there's another coming from Arts and Monuments who's neither a dealer nor a collector, just a professor of the history of art. I think we can rely on him. At the moment, though, we're a little busy with a few other things that have turned up.'

Back at the flat, she made coffee from the American K ration sachets that Pugh was always being given, and they sat drinking quietly. As the minutes passed, he noticed she was not anxious to go to bed and he realised she was afraid.

After a while, he went to the bedroom. She gave him a nervous glance but it changed as he emerged with an army blanket, which he tossed on the settee.

'You must be tired,' he said. 'The bed's all yours. Lock the door if it pleases you.'

She blushed. 'I'm sorry, Piu,' she said. 'I didn't trust you. I shall not lock the door. I think you are a good man.'

Pugh grinned. 'Perhaps you'd better, all the same. I might be good but I'm not saintly.'

That made her smile, but she rose and headed for the bedroom. 'It is good here,' she said. 'I feel safe.'

The following morning, Pugh woke to find her fully dressed beside the settee, holding out a cup of coffee.

'For you. I think I must now go to the hospital.'

He sat up, allowing the blanket to slide to the floor. 'Don't speak to any strange men.'

'I shall keep myself only for you, Piu.'

During the day, Pugh went along to Tassinari's to find Marco. The old lawyer was working at a big desk in his chilly room. Despite the sunshine, his fleshless fingers looked blue with cold.

'I have worked out the estate,' he said. 'I have it all down.'

'Is there anything apart from the paintings?'

'Nothing. I suspect Marco was selling off his brother's belongings during the whole of his last illness. He probably has quite a lot of money salted away.'

Pugh looked about him. 'Where *is* Marco?'

Tassinari shrugged. 'He left. In disgust, I think. He said he was going to the Galleria Umberto. He's probably trying to sell a few small treasures that he managed to hide from us.'

The Galleria Umberto was the geographical and spiritual heart of Naples. A vast, cavernous glass-roofed cross made up of four wide arcades and a central hall lined with shops, cafés, bars and billiard saloons, it was the trysting place for any Neapolitan engaged in business, legal or otherwise. Its small café tables were ideal for discussions, the tiny cups of coffee, their price inevitably high, the statutory fee for their use.

Under the great canopy, you could see a film, do your shopping, get a cure for syphilis or pick up a woman.

263

You could also give away a fortune to the beggars, because the gallery was full of them, and they were the most pathetic in the whole of Italy. They always had been and now, since the liberation, they were even more so. There were mothers with babies at the breast and toddlers clinging to their skirts, and hordes of un-attached children who appeared from nowhere, silent and unspeaking, holding out theirs hands for alms. Pugh had often heard it said that mothers borrowed each other's babies to beg there and that they pinched their bottoms to make them cry, but the pathos was such that though Naples was the most depraved city in Europe, Pugh had never entirely believed it. Since he was known there and recognised as a soft touch, the children crowded round him holding out their hands with a murmured 'Ho fame' – I'm hungry. Among them was a youngster with a peg-leg to replace the one cut off by a tram, and Pugh dished out a few coins to assuage the guilt he felt. The German and Allied occupations had destroyed morals more thoroughly than bombs had destroyed houses. There were hard-faced small boys who had lived on their wits ever since they could walk; carrying little trays on which American cigarettes were laid out separately for sale, with contraceptives and dirty postcards; or pimping for their sisters, who worked from one of the cafés or walked up and down the long arcades arm-in-arm studying prospective customers with bold eyes.

Walking past the shops selling hats – of which there seemed plenty – and clothes – of which there seemed hardly any at all – and past the religious images and souvenirs, he spotted Marco Detto Banti in a shop whose window contained a single strip of red velvet, on which were posed a few fragments of jewellery and silver that looked very much like the treasured possessions of Neapolitans who had been obliged to sell them to stay alive.

On the counter between the owner of the shop and

Marco Detto Banti was a small bronze figurine, and they seemed to be having a furious argument about its value. Neither of them noticed Pugh enter the shop until he put his hand on the figurine, then the shopkeeper reached under the counter for a weapon. As Marco started to bolt, Pugh grabbed his collar, holding him as he turned to the shopkeeper.

'If that's a gun,' he said, 'you'd better leave it where it is. I suspect that what's being offered has been stolen, so you won't be interested, will you?'

The shopkeeper straightened up, shaking his head vigorously, and, picking up the figurine, Pugh pushed Marco outside. He made no further attempt to escape, merely following dejectedly as Pugh made his way to a bar. Finding a table, he sat down and gestured to Marco to do the same. He indicated the figurine.

'It belonged to Bocco, didn't it?' he said.

Marco nodded.

'So, technically, it's not yours to sell. It belongs to Bocco's daughter, doesn't it?'

Another nod.

'Are there any others?'

'One or two.'

'I'll come and collect them.' Pugh ordered drinks then leaned forward. 'As it happens, though, I'm more interested in something else. Someone tried to kill me last night. He was waiting for me. He had an address in his pocket. Tamara's address. Did you give it to someone?'

'No, I swear. On my dead mother's grave!'

'Come off it, Marco. Tell the truth.'

Marco subsided and the nod came again.

'Who?'

'An American. I thought it might make a little money. They promised me a cut.'

'On what?'

'The pictures.'

'You don't know where they are.'

265

'I thought they'd know how to find out.'

Pugh exploded. 'You bastard! You gave them that address so they'd pick up Tamara! They'd have beaten her up for it, perhaps even tortured her. They'd have done for both of us.' Pugh grabbed at Marco so angrily that the waiter who was just arriving with the drinks backed away hurriedly. Pugh looked up, slammed Marco back into his seat and paid for the drinks. 'Who was it you told?'

'An American officer.'

'Who?'

'I don't know his name.'

'Was it Baracca?'

'I think that was his name, but I'm not sure.'

'Why did you think *he'd* be interested?'

'Because he's a crook.'

'How do you know?'

'I saw him in Vicinamontane. Before my brother died. Talking to Sansovino, the Mayor, on the steps of the Palazzo Municipale. They seemed to be organising something.'

'How do you know?'

'Because he came more than once.'

Pugh frowned. No wonder the word had got around quickly that there were Detto Bantis available. If Baracca had been in Vicinamontane, he would inevitably have heard of them.

'Did *you* tell him there were paintings?'

'No.'

Pugh leaned forward. 'Tell me the truth or I'll have you arrested for trying to sell stolen goods belonging to a British citizen we're interested in.'

'Bocco wasn't British. He renounced his citizenship.'

'We'd arrange to have him de-renounce it. Did you?'

'I might have done. I met him once. In the bar.'

'So it was you who started the hue and cry about the Detto Bantis. I ought to beat your head flat, Marco. On the other hand' – Pugh reached out and swallowed his

266

drink – 'perhaps not. Thanks to you, we found out who the Detto Bantis belong to. How did you know Baracca was in Naples? Did he tell you?'

'No. I saw him here in the Galleria. With a British officer. I came down to try to – sell something, and I saw him.'

'Doing what?'

'Drinking. Just drinking. What else would he be doing?'

Pugh frowned. 'He might have been trying to sell the bloody Galleria, for all we know,' he said.

Captain Jones whistled when Pugh told him what he'd learned.

'Baracca,' he said slowly. 'Think he's the one supplying Tirandolo?'

'It's obvious what the bastard was up to,' Pugh said. 'And this was going to be a put-up job like the Focchias in Rome. Two bodies. A hopeless love affair.'

'You?' Jones laughed. 'A love affair? You're not the type.'

'Maybe not. But who'd know that but you and me? They were after the whereabouts of the pictures and they'd just have left us to be found. Star-crossed bloody lovers in a suicide pact.'

Jones frowned. 'I think we have to tread carefully,' he said. 'We've got to be certain where we're going. I wonder if we ought to warn Tasker, after all.'

Pugh shook his head. 'I think it would be better if we kept him out of it,' he said.

'He'll play hell when he finds out.'

'Let him. He's a pal of Baracca's and he might just let something slip. Besides, I'm looking forward to seeing his face when we tell him. "Sir, your old buddy, Colonel Arnold J. Baracca, US army, has been arrested. The charges are conspiracy and complicity in fraud and murder."'

They discussed the aspects of the case and Jones

eventually agreed to go above Tasker's head to the general.

'He'll probably push me on to the brigadier,' he said. 'Because everybody's getting ready for the move north of Rome. But the brig won't let us down.' He sat back and stared at Pugh. 'My God, this thing's blown up, hasn't it? Da Sangalla and De Castro arrested, Corneliano shot dead, and your friend Tirandolo already in custody. Now Baracca. We'll end up with half Italy behind bars at this rate. How do you want to work it?'

'I'm going to keep an eye on where Baracca goes. We might even find out who his contacts are.'

'Not you,' Jones said. 'O'Mara. They know you too well, and they might take the opportunity to bump you off.'

When Pugh called later in the day at the *questura*, the police officer, Zolli, happened to be there.

He grinned at Pugh. 'Papagallo,' he said. 'Furio Papagallo. Known as Capatosta – Hard Head. The man who attacked you. We identified him. He's in with the gangs. We've had him in our sights for some time over a few missing people. I think you've done us a favour.'

On his way back to Casa Calafati, Pugh drove past Tasker's office. Not unexpectedly, Tasker's car was outside the O Sole Mio bar and, as usual, Cirri's horse was tied to the lamp post.

Sergeant O'Mara was sitting in another bar further down the street. 'He's in there, boyo,' he said.

'Who's with him?'

'Himself – Tasker. They have the drink taken. The undertaker feller, Cirri, and Brother Gregorio, the guardian of the catacombs, are there, too.' He grinned at Pugh's expression. 'Catholic priests like a drink now and then, boyo. Sure, this one does, anyway.'

It sounded a disappointing gathering. Pugh had half expected Sansovino or one of the other big names from the Naples gangland. Perhaps even Genovese himself.

It was late when Pugh returned to the Casa Calafati, so he entered quietly. Tamara had obviously been waiting for him because she was stretched out on the settee, her face in the cushion, her hair like lace across her cheek, her lashes like small fans against her skin. Over her face was a copy of *Domenica del Corriere*, the sensation magazine all Italians seemed to love. The cover depicted a nun being savaged by a wolf.

As he bent over, she stirred and turned on her back, blinking at the light. As she focused and finally saw him, she came awake immediately and her mouth widened in that warm grin of hers, then unexpectedly, instinctively, she flung her arms round his neck and hugged him with such a spontaneous demonstration of relief he felt desperately touched.

For a moment they clung to each other, then she pushed him away, blushing through her laughter.

'Forgive me, Piu! I was worried. And when it grew late I was afraid. They decided at the hospital to pay me for all the time I was away and I bought meat. Not much, but I was going to cook a meal for you when you arrived. Unfortunately, I fell asleep.'

He placed the figurine he had obtained from Marco on the table alongside her.

'A bit more of your past,' he said. 'I found it in the Galleria Umberto. It belonged to your father.'

'How do you know?'

'I spotted Marco trying to sell it. There won't be much else now, though, apart from the canvasses.'

As he leaned over her he could feel the warmth of her skin and began to think of things that he'd been trying to push to the back of his mind for some time.

'You smell good,' he said.

'It is French perfume. Black market. Very expensive. I bought it today. With the money they gave me. After the meal I shall have to eat nothing but bread and olive oil for a week.' She looked at him, her eyes big and knowing and spiky with long lashes. 'I think you are thinking things, Piu,' she said.

'It doesn't require much imagination.'

She grinned. 'I thought you were a gentleman.'

'Even gentlemen are known to behave out of character.'

They were both skirting round the subject because neither wished to make the first move, then she gave a happy little laugh.

'I think you are trying to tell me something,' she said.

'I didn't think you'd notice.'

They stared at each other for a long painful moment, Pugh flushed, Tamara with a grave expression that was belied by sparkling eyes. Suddenly tears appeared.

'What's the matter?'

'I'm so happy. I can't help it.'

As she made a grab for him, he fell across her on the settee. As she squirmed away from him, the bronze figurine fell to the carpet.

'It will break,' she said, reaching for it.

'Not it.'

As he hauled her back, the alarm in her voice died quickly. The fight she put up against his hands was only half-hearted.

Her mouth was by his ear. 'I saw the look your Sergeant O'Mara gave you in the restaurant,' she said. 'I think he was right.'

Pugh shrugged. 'Paddy O'Mara's Irish,' he pointed out. 'And the Irish are supposed to have the gift of second sight.'

11

For once everybody was doing all right. Patrick Fitzgerald O'Mara had long since come to the conclusion that the girl in his rooms would fit splendidly into the village in Galway where he lived, and, as a good Catholic, would be approved of by his family and the village priest. Sergeant Plummer had finally decided that he would marry his girl when he finally got around to it – if he didn't change his mind in the meantime and go home instead to the girl who was waiting for him in Lancashire. Even Captain Jones was satisfied. He had recently met an Italian 'contessa' at a party in one of the neighbouring officers' messes and they were getting along like a house on fire.

'My mother was English,' she had announced. 'And when my father was killed in the desert I decided I would like to go to England.' He didn't believe her for a minute but that was the way it went with Italian 'contessas'.

The conversation Pugh was conducting with Tamara Detto Banti was also following an expected course. She was clinging to him, flushed and happy, her doubts about her morals thrust firmly into the background, while Pugh was reflecting what a source of contentment it was to be certain of someone, with no qualifications attached and no holds barred. He found that he was enjoying having her there to return to. She seemed to fill up some of the emptiness there had always been in his life and provided some of the warmth that had always been lacking.

'Happy?' he asked.

'Yes, Piu.'

'When I'm an old man will you still call me, "Piu"?'

'It is how I know you. To me you will always be caro Piu.'

'I think you had your eye on me all along.'

'Not really. From the second day in Vicinamontane. At first I thought you were *odioso* – hateful.'

'I was being a very proper lawyer-like lawyer-type, as well as a very straightforward and soldierly security sergeant-type concerned with duty. Mind you, I began to get ideas after we shared the curtain a few times. This isn't the first time you've slept with me, remember.'

'I think you showed much fortitude.' She wriggled in the circle of his arm. 'I have a day off today. Can you not telephone the army and tell them you have a bad leg?'

'We have things to do. There are pictures to identify for a start!'

She gave him a worried look. 'You will take care? There may be more men with knives. Can you not delay a little?'

'There's plenty of time.' He put his arms round her. 'You know, I feel this is right.'

'That I am in bed with you?'

'Your mother,' he pointed out, 'got into bed with Bocco Detto Banti.'

As Pugh headed for Jones's office the following morning, he met the old man who lived behind the Pizzoni Palace and kept himself alive by carving cigarette holders, statues of saints and candlesticks from old bones. Pugh greeted him cheerfully, feeling on top of the world, but the old man merely shook his head.

'*Sono fottuto*,' he said. 'I am ruined! I can no longer collect my bones from the San Placido catacombs. The monks have always allowed me to but now they've stopped me, and I have to go to San Gennaro and I'm too old to walk that far.'

'Why have they stopped you?'

'I was told by Brother Gregorio that it is the

272

desecration of a sacred place. I didn't believe him. I think he has started selling the bones to someone else.'

Pugh gave him the few coins that were in his pocket to help him buy food, reflecting that, as Tamara had often said, every day in Naples was a crisis day.

When he arrived in front of Jones, he found him in an enthusiastic mood.

'I saw the general,' he said. 'He put me on to the brigadier. I thought he would. But the brig thinks anyone who steals from the army is a crook – which, of course, they are – and the thought that his boys are having to do without things because they're going into the dirty mitts of Italian gangsters and their pals gets him breathing fire and slaughter. He says we can call on the military police. On the Brigade of Guards, if necessary. We'll keep the carabinieri out of it. Somebody might talk. When do we move? We could hide everybody in the catacombs if we wish.'

Pugh frowned as a thought occurred to him. He had a sudden suspicion that the O Sole Mio bar was probably a staging post for whatever was coming from Africa. It was a perfect place, and Baracca used it a lot. And on his way back to Naples from Vicinamontane, hadn't he seen the undertaker, Cirri, heading out into the country where he ought never to have been? Was *he* involved? Was he doing the same thing they had been doing, and using coffins to carry goods in secret? It was more than possible. If Pugh could use a hearse to fool people, so could Cirri.

'Let's pick him up quietly,' he said. 'Then announce we're going to make a raid on the O Sole Mio bar. You never know what we might stir up. We might be surprised whom we rope in.'

Jones looked at him quizzically. 'Who are you thinking of?'

'An undertaker for a start. The one who handled the Grei funeral. He must have known that coffin he provided was too big. So why did he provide it?'

273

'They'd never store the stuff at the O Sole Mio, for God's sake! Too many officers use it.'

'No, but there are a lot of good places nearby. Let's start the panic and see where they all start running to.'

It was decided to pick up Baracca at the American mess the following day, and Sergeant O'Mara was sent to make sure he went there for the evening. An informer was to be let out early the following morning to call in at the O Sole Mio bar in a state of great excitement to make it known that a raid was in the offing.

For Pugh's evening meal Tamara provided something that looked and smelled like goulash, and he took home a bottle of wine. She was alongside him almost before he shut the door, kissing him and taking his briefcase.

'Have you got the expert yet to look at the pictures?' she asked.

'He's due any day. So is Tassinari's man. You'll soon have some idea how much you're worth.'

'Do you have to go out again?'

'Not tonight. And I have a great capacity for shoving the day's business under the carpet when I'm home.'

At midnight the telephone rang. Pugh disentangled himself and went to answer it. It was O'Mara.

'Baracca,' he said. 'He didn't go back to the mess, boyo. He had a woman in his car when he left the Alexa Hotel. They've gone to her place. 'Tis my guess he won't be reappearing.'

'Keep an eye on it, Paddy,' Pugh said. 'I'll contact Jones and we'll pick him up in the early hours. I'll be in the office in half an hour's time.'

Tamara was sitting up when he returned. 'I have to go out after all,' he said, pleased to see the disappointment in her face. 'This time tomorrow,' he said, 'it'll all be over.'

She shrugged. 'Nothing is ever over in Naples.'

Jones was waiting at the office with the colonel in command of the provost department, and a colonel called Checker from the American Intelligence Service who was surrounded by men who looked like FBI agents out of an old film. The American looked at his watch as Pugh entered.

'All right,' Jones said briskly. 'Let's go and pick him up. We've got enough rank with us. He'll not be able to complain.' He smiled at Checker. 'Since he's your responsiblity, we'll leave it to you.'

Checker nodded. 'Right,' he said.

Baracca's woman had an apartment near the Via Roma. It was in a large, expensive block, which, considering the condition of Naples, was surprisingly luxurious. Pugh wondered how much Baracca subsidised her and how much she drew from other activities. As they paused outside the door, Checker glanced round him.

'Ready?'

'Okay.'

Checker's big fist on the door was enough to wake the dead, and they immediately heard sounds of alarm inside.

'Open up!' Checker roared. 'Before we break the door down!'

The door was opened slowly. Inside the room, Baracca was standing in his trousers and shirt and without shoes, and looked as if he had flung his clothes on in a hurry. 'What the hell is this?' he demanded.

Checker pushed past him. 'Never mind that,' he snapped. 'We've every right to be here.'

'What's it all about, for Christ's sake?'

'You're under arrest, Colonel. I'm Colonel Checker, of Intelligence, so your escort will be of equal rank.'

Baracca had gone pale and seemed suddenly shrunken and old. 'Why am I under arrest? What are the charges?'

'Conspiracy. Handling stolen US army stores. There are a few others, too, but they'll do to be going on with, I guess. You'll hear 'em all in due time.'

Baracca's girl friend pushed forward, a small woman

275

with blonde hair that didn't seem to go with her eyes and dark skin. 'Leave my home at once,' she said loudly. 'I am the Contessa Giuccoli.'

'Ma'am,' Checker said in a bored voice, 'you're all goddam contessas.'

Her eyes flashed with fury. 'I am a personal friend of Brigadier-General Hosey.'

'Ma'am, so am I.'

'And he's in constant touch with—'

Checker stopped her dead. 'Ma'am, I don't give a good goddam if he's in touch with the Lord Jesus H. Christ. Your friend here's under arrest and, since you're probably in cahoots with him, you'd better come too. I can't see how in hell you manage to live here if you aren't.'

Baracca was escorted to the car and whisked away to be cross-examined and charged. To their surprise, the woman really was a countess, but it didn't take them five minutes to discover she had been accepting stolen US army clothing all the same, and turning it over to the black market.

'Every bastard in Naples is at it,' Checker growled.

With Baracca locked up, they sat around smoking and drinking coffee until dawn, waiting until the streets began to become alive.

'I want to catch Cirri red-handed,' Jones announced.

Eventually they headed for the Piazza San Placido and, taking up positions, sent their informer into the O Sole Mio with his warning of a raid. The place was just opening for early morning coffees and for a long time nothing happened. Then they saw Cirri's hearse appear at a fast trot and stop outside. Cirri, who was driving, almost fell from the box in his haste and started to back the hearse into the yard behind the bar.

''Tis a quare feller for an undertaker, that one,' O'Mara observed.

The owner of the bar appeared and gestured wildly at

Cirri, clearly urging him to hurry.

'He hasn't taken the nag out of the harness for once,' Pugh pointed out.

'I reckon 'tis a quick getaway he's intendin',' O'Mara said. 'They're stuffin' things into the old hearse as if they're expectin' th' end o' the world. Do we pick him up?'

'Let him move off first. Let him get round the corner. He'll not have a leg to stand on. Then we'll move into the bar.'

As O'Mara stepped out in front of the hearse, Cirri climbed down and wilted against the wheel as if he were about to collapse.

'Okay,' Jones said, lifting his walkie-talkie. 'We'll move in on the bar now.'

Before he could speak, however, Pugh banged his shoulder.

'Hang on,' he said. 'What's this?'

A British army staff car was roaring up the hill to stop outside the bar. The man who jumped out was Tasker.

'He must have heard, after all,' Jones observed.

Tasker disappeared inside the bar but, before they could move, he reappeared with the owner, jumped into his car and hurtled across the square to the Church of San Placido. Leaping out again, he disappeared round the back of the church to where the entrance to the catacombs lay.

'What in God's name . . . ?'

Jones looked at Pugh, who was frowning deeply, his mind suddenly full of what the old man who lived behind the Pizzoni Palace had said – the old man who had been deprived of the bone which was the raw material of his small craftsmanship – that the monk responsible for shutting the catacombs to him was Brother Gregorio, who was often in the O Sole Mio bar at the same time as Tasker and Baracca.

'By God!' he yelled. 'Of course! The catacombs! That bloody monk detests visitors! I always thought it was because he didn't like people. But it's not that at all. It's because of what's inside.'

San Placido was only a small part of the Neapolitan catacombs, which were among the most extensive in Italy, and possibly the world. Within minutes, cars, police vans and trucks were drawing to a stop outside the entrance. Using the radio to contact Checker, they had quickly built up an emergency force of sixty men, including Italian police, British Field Security men and American Counter-Intelligence agents, to cover all possible exits. As they gathered, fifteen Jeep-loads of men coming to a halt by the entrance to the catacombs, loaded down with cave exploration gear and enough weapons to tackle a German division, Tasker's camouflaged Humber was still waiting and empty, the engine still running. As Pugh reached over to switch it off, the monks who were responsible for the catacombs appeared, alarmed and hostile to the invasion.

'This is nothing but an intrusion into a sacred place,' one of them said angrily.

'Never mind that,' Pugh said. 'We have questions to ask. There's a man in there and we need to make a check.'

'This is not a battlefield,' the monk snapped. 'The catacombs are well known and we are constantly having visitors.'

'This visitor's a senior British officer.'

The monk sniffed. 'He is well known to us. He seems to like the catacombs and he is always *simpatico* and generous with money.'

'I'll bet he is,' Pugh said. 'Let's have Brother Gregorio out here. He's the man who always shows him round, I expect.'

It took some time to locate Brother Gregorio, who was found eventually hiding in a store room. As he appeared, his face was dark with anger and, planting himself across the entrance, he had to be removed by force.

'Is there anyone in there now with Tasker?' Pugh demanded.

The monk refused to answer and they could only assume that there was. As they tried to push past, Brother Gregorio broke free and sailed into them, fists swinging in a most unlikely demonstration of brotherly love. A helmet clanked to the ground, then one of the Americans got his arm round Gregorio's neck and squeezed until the monk went red in the face.

'He's probably in the game, too,' Pugh said. 'Even the bloody priests aren't as honest as they might be these days.'

'Okay,' Colonel Checker said. 'Take the sonofabitch away.'

As Gregorio was pulled aside, protesting loudly in a resounding condemnation of their desecration of a holy place, it was discovered that, though the catacombs had always been open to visitors, no one had any idea of how the corridors and chambers ran, and a police Jeep was sent off to headquarters to try to find a map.

Even when it arrived there was no knowing how accurate it was, after damage by past earth tremors, eruptions of Vesuvius, and the various subsidences that had followed.

For a while they crowded round the map, trying to decide if the reports of knocking they'd received in the past had anything to do with what they now knew, and whether they really had been caused by Germans or by gangsters hiding their loot down there.

There were two networks of catacombs, and the one at the back of the Church of San Placido was believed to date from the second century after Christ. Colonel Checker was awed.

'Holy Jesus Christ,' he said. 'That old?'

The catacombs consisted of several galleries, excavated one below the other, each with numerous branches and parallel passages. Two of the galleries had crumbled and had not been accessible since the turn of the century.

They were still uncertain what they expected to find and Gregorio was dragged forward again, spluttering with rage. He refused to talk, and it was only when he was threatened with everything under the sun that he admitted that things 'had been hidden in the catacombs'.

'What things?' Pugh demanded.

The monk refused to say, and it was hard to tell if he knew. But it was possible, from what he said, to identify Cirri, the undertaker, the owner of the O Sole Mio, Baracca and Colonel Tasker.

It was late in the day when they finally entered the catacombs, equipped with American lamps. Gregorio's clear guilt had stirred up a show of conscience among the other monks, and two of them, both young, agreed to lead the way. As they went in, they heard the low wail of the air raid sirens.

'Oh, shit!' Checker said. 'A lousy air raid! Do we call it off?'

'Not damn likely,' Pugh said hotly. 'We've got this far. If we go for the shelters the buggers will escape. We take our chances. Everybody else's taking chances. So will we.'

Checker grinned. 'Okay, son. If the bastards drop a bomb on us we'll be buried in bones. Christ, what an end!'

Outside, the streets were filling with people hurrying for the shelters. Women with wailing babies screamed as they ran. Stern-faced policemen directed them. A man was dragging a mule by its halter, cursing in purple phrases as it refused to hurry. Military vehicles bolted away and the street was full of the clatter of running feet.

The walls of the ante-rooms they had to pass through to reach the galleries of the catacombs were covered in painted designs. They were in excellent condition considering they had been there for centuries, and they gave the impression of enormous altarpieces with pictures of saints and martyrs. As they entered the catacombs proper, the chattering voices became silent.

280

Almost at once they found themselves facing what appeared to be a huge catafalque covered with a rotting pall decorated with death's heads. About it, walls painted to represent marble curved behind faked alabaster pillars up to sculpted ceilings of simulated gilt lattice-work. Bronze statues on corner pedestals and suits of armour in niches, surrounded by the spiky military bouquets of swords, banners, breast plates, drums and trumpets, proved to be nothing more than painted high-relief plaster mouldings. Mock mirrors threw back counterfeit images of the opposite walls in weird optical illusions, and even the worn stone floors showed where they had once been painted to represent ancient mosaics. Here and there patches of damp had damaged the painting, occasionally gilt had flaked from a corner or rats had eaten a hole in the wainscoting, but the general effect, shabby, ornate and grotesque, still remained of a huge, over-decorated family tomb.

Beyond, in a deeper gallery, there were rows of what looked like small chapels, each cut one above the other in the walls and all crammed to the ceiling with skeletons.

'Holy Jesus Christ,' Checker said. 'Where do they all come from?'

'They don't bury them,' Pugh explained, 'they rent a wall niche for ten, twenty-five or fifty years, but less than ten if they haven't much money. Then the body's removed and buried, the coffin broken up and burned and, after a further four years, they dig up the bones and shove 'em in here.'

Checker looked awed. 'Holy Jesus Christ,' he said again.

'Most of these,' one of the monks said, 'are plague victims, placed here after the earthquake and plague at the turn of the century. Many also come from sixteenth-century outbreaks.'

Checker picked up a skull. 'Alas, poor Yorick,' he said and one of the monks behind him snatched it angrily from him.

The American reacted with a burst of bad temper of

his own. 'Have there been Germans in here?' he snapped.

The monks answered evasively, in a way that made them feel sure there had.

'What about now? What's in here now?'

The monks shrugged, saying they thought *something* was there but they didn't know what, and in the next gallery they found a stack of suitcases piled against the wall.

'Bring those lights over here.'

The suitcases were locked but an American sergeant forced them open one after another. They were crammed with penicillin, in solution and as powder, and phials of morphine.

'Christ,' Checker said. 'A thousand guys could die for want of this goddam stuff!' He gestured at the sergeant. 'We'll be making a search afterwards and we'll be wanting to interrogate every goddam man who ever came in here, monk or no monk. We'll have the goddam Pope if he's guilty.'

They closed the cases and left a couple of men to guard them, and there was a brief silence as they wondered which way to go next. As they waited, there was a sudden rattle ahead of them in the darkness, and a cry, then briefly they saw the flash of a torch.

'There they are, the sonsabitches!' Checker yelled.

'Wait! Wait!' The two monks seemed horrified. 'There are terrible dangers! You must not hurry!'

It seemed that in the close bone-crammed galleries beneath the city there were dozens of side turnings, each with many dark vaults, in any of which the men they were seeking could be hidden. As they paused, wondering what to do next, they heard a thump which seemed to come through the very bones of the earth and the faint thud of guns. They all looked at each other nervously.

'Bombs,' Jones said. 'Jerry's arrived.'

They waited, listening, as more thumps occurred.

They appeared to shake the earth around them and after one, which sounded particularly near, several bones slid from a shelf to the ground. Checker began to grow irritable.

'We musn't hurry,' the monks said again. 'We must move carefully. And by the map.'

'Jesus,' Checker said. 'I wouldn't like to be down here if my torch battery gave out.'

The thought seemed to start a train of thought in his mind and he ordered half his men to switch off their lights, just in case.

They were in a chill, damp vault with an earthen floor now. On one side skulls were piled neatly in long rows two feet high, on the other was a great barricade of leg and arm bones held in place by a tangle of vertebrae, broken pelvises and shoulder-blades. A wall had collapsed at one end and the remains of generation on generation of Neapolitans lay in tumbled heaps.

There were chapels full of bones, all that was left of thousands of people, all carefully dismembered, assorted and even arranged into designs as if they were beads. Here the walls were lined with pelvic girdles, laid one on another like tiles on a roof, there ribs were fashioned into bowers, and femurs into crucifixes, with the vertebrae arranged like mosaics, like rosettes, flutings, chains, twining hearts.

'Holy Jesus Christ,' Checker said once more. 'What sort of mentality was behind this lot?'

One of the monks sniffed. 'It is our purpose to remember that we must die,' he said. 'We wish to remind all who come here of our own mortality, of the futility of life on earth.'

Checker stared at him as if he had crawled out of a hole. In his greyish robe, in fact, he looked like a mole, grovelling under the earth among human bones for the glory of God, and it occurred to Pugh that the Neapolitans, living in constant intimacy with death – one only had to see the daily parade of hearses across the city to know it was never far from their minds – didn't much need reminding of mortality.

For what seemed hours, they crept about among the bones, constantly coming upon new designs of rib bones and skulls. Round every corner there was something fresh. They had been awed into silence by now and not a sound had been heard for some time, then, with shocking suddenness, there was a long burst of fire from what appeared to be a light machine gun. The noise echoed and re-echoed, clattering about them like thunder.

One of the American soldiers yelped and fell, then a whole avalanche of bones came down as a shelf collapsed and swept them aside. Flinging himself down among them, Pugh half expected them to smell, but there was only the scent of dryness, dust and age. As they rose warily, the machine gun fired again and they flung themselves down once more, indifferent to the remnants of mortality about them.

'Keep those goddam lights down,' Checker snarled as the lamps swept round, making the grinning death's heads seem alive. Sure enough, there was another burst of fire that brought plaster and fragments of stone down on them. A falling skull clonked on a steel helmet. Then, as the lights were doused, leaving them all in a thick darkness, they waited with thumping hearts, wondering what lay ahead.

Behind them, the American soldier, who had been hit in the thigh, was being laid out on the floor. 'For Christ's sake, don't leave me here,' he was begging.

As they held their breath, they heard running feet and, as they pushed the bones aside and the lights were dragged forward and switched on again, they saw Tasker moving in erratic fashion ahead of them. Just behind him was the shadowy shape of the owner of the O Sole Mio and another man. As the lights caught them, they turned, and for a second their faces showed white and startled.

'Halt,' Checker yelled. 'Stop right there!'

The faces vanished as the hurrying figures turned away again, and Checker yelled, 'Get the bastards!'

But, as he shouted, there was a crash and a clatter, followed by a long surging sound as tons of bones slid forward. They saw Tasker turn again and open his mouth in a scream, then he was swept away as the piles of human debris smashed into him. There was another crash, then a huge puff of dust like an explosion, and they heard him cry out, despairing, almost shrieking. A rumbling sound followed, then a moan, and then silence. For a long time they remained still, their faces lit by the lamps they carried, as they stared in awe at each other.

The dust seemed to hang in the gallery for a long time, a huge grey-yellow cloud, filling the air and making them cough and choke and spit as it filled their mouths and eyes. As it subsided and the gallery slowly became visible again, Pugh pointed ahead.

'Take care,' one of the monks said. 'Something has given way.'

'It sure has,' Checker growled.

Crawling along, groping among the collapsed piles of bones, aware of terrible unseen dangers, they came to the torrent of bones lying like the bricks of a collapsed house. Just beyond it was a yawning black hole. The whole floor in front of them had caved in and fallen away. Creeping gingerly forward, they shone the lights into the hole, but all they could see below them was a pile of ancient rib bones, pelvises, femurs and skulls, from which protruded bricks and timbers.

Checker peered down. 'Tasker, you bastard,' he called. 'You down there?'

There was no sound, and he turned to the men behind him. 'Microphone,' he said.

Clambering over the avalanche of the remains of dead human beings, which clattered as if they were loosely stacked coal, someone brought batteries and earphones forward. The microphone was dangled into the hole but the silence was complete.

As they listened, Pugh was reminded of mine rescue films he'd seen. They sat for a long time with ears cocked, listening for the faintest sign of life. But there was nothing, only the empty darkness, a silence as thick as velvet, and echoes whenever anybody moved or spoke.

'Can we get gown there?' Jones demanded.

The monks shook their heads. 'There is no chance,' one of them said. 'The whole of this gallery is unsafe. You were warned.'

'I know we were goddam warned,' Checker snapped. 'But we've got a job to do. We want to get someone down there.'

'You would be putting his life in great danger.'

Eventually they came to the conclusion that Tasker was either unconscious or dead, and that it would need more than the equipment they had with them to find out. Checker coughed, clearing his throat as if it were choked with the dust of long-dead people.

'Okay,' he said. 'I guess that's it. We'll not get 'em outa there in a hurry.'

The air raid had ended when they reappeared in the street. They could hear the grind of ambulances and the wail of their sirens, and over the houses they could see rising columns of smoke where the bombs had fallen.

A guard was set at the entrance to the catacombs and a team was whistled up to question the monks more closely. Eventually ropes and climbing gear were produced and an attempt was made to get into the hole. But then another portion of the passageway crumbled and fell away and the monks again warned that more still could go, so that Checker finally called off the operation.

'I'm not having my guys hurt to rescue those bastards,' he said. 'Not in that goddam morbid necrophilic hole.'

Most of them remained there for the rest of the night, just a few men stationed deep inside, but nothing was reported, no sound, no light, no voices, no movement. The O Sole Mio was silent and dark and Colonel Tasker's car remained unclaimed and was eventually driven off. The suitcases were examined and assessed and orders were issued to pick up Sansovino and all his associates. Baracca was brought up under escort and Checker tore him off a strip.

'Paintings,' he snarled. 'Drugs from the sick and dying! Did you want every goddam bit of loot in Italy for yourself? Guys like you are getting the US a bad name.'

There had been no more sound from the catacombs and they could only assume that the cry they had heard and the crash and clatter of the avalanche of ancient bones had been the end of Tasker and his companions. No one expected them to reappear.

'"Killed on active service!"' Pugh said dryly. 'That's how he'll appear in the casualty lists.'

As the search was called off, Jones drove him back to the office in the Jeep. O'Mara, who had been sent back to hold the fort, said the air raid had been bad.

''Twas a terrible hard one,' he said. 'They've reported over a hundred casualties, and buildings are down in the Capodimonte and Mergellina districts.'

Tired, his face strained and grey with exhaustion, his clothes and hair covered with dust, Pugh started the motor bike and rode slowly back towards the Casa Calafati. As he passed the Via Villari, he noticed the air was full of smoke and he could smell burning, and he decided to stop to see if old Mori and the paintings were safe.

The area was full of rubble. A house seemed to have been ripped apart and the whole façade lay in the street, smoke still seeping through the brickwork. A policeman was keeping people away in case of unexploded bombs, and Pugh rode round the block to approach it from the other side. Another policeman agreed to keep an eye on the motor cycle, and Pugh picked his way through the bricks and pieces of broken masonry, splintered timber, glass, scattered fragments of clothing and fluttering scraps of paper.

Agente di Pompe Funebri Mori was standing in the street with Foscari, his face grey with weariness. He was standing by his cart, his old horse, Urbino, dozing quietly in the shafts. Across the white plaster dust that covered his face were runnels where the tears had coursed.

'All gone, Signore,' he said. 'All gone!'

'They killed Fiorello,' Foscari said, pointing.

The old horse lay on its side, half-covered with rubble, its eyes glazed with a faint blue film, dried blood round the open mouth from which a large pink tongue lolled.

Poor old Fiorello, Pugh thought. The horse had served them well. It was a pity he had had to die from a chance German bomb that was probably aimed at the docks.

'*È solo la forza del destino.*' Foscari's optimism was strong, his courage uplifting. 'We'll rebuild. I'm young and I know how to lay bricks. And there are plenty about for the taking. I have my tools. We still have Urbino and we'll soon find another hearse.'

Pugh whirled. 'Another hearse? What happened to the one we've got?'

'It's gone,' Mori mourned. 'Your secrets have disappeared.'

Foscari pulled a face. 'I think everything we did was for nothing,' he said slowly.

He gestured to Pugh to follow him. All round them were black charred beams and scorched bricks and stones. A wall had fallen, hiding the yard, but as they picked their way past, Pugh saw Ciasca's old hearse that had carried them all the way from Vicinamontane. It was standing in the middle of the wreckage among blazing furniture and crackling timbers that had once been a roof. Through its plate glass sides, Pugh could see the coffin. His heart sank and he felt suddenly numb, as though everything had been drained out of him. Everything they had struggled for was disappearing before his eyes.

Because of the searing heat it was impossible to approach nearer than ten metres and, rubbing his eyes against the smoke, he fell back with the others as a fresh burst of flame lifted. The whole interior of the hearse was smoking now, the black varnish running down its sides. The solid rubber tyres on the tall rear wheels had already melted, and suddenly a plate-glass panel cracked with a report like a pistol shot and one of the corner lanterns flopped over and began to change shape. The coffin started to burn furiously.

As he watched, a low warning rumble came from the heart of the fire and the few watching people drew back. The whole front of the building began to lean forward slowly, as if it were bowing, then it crashed down, burying the hearse under tons of blazing rubble. A column of fire lifted in a huge billow of orange towards the sky, then the fallen masonry and woodwork settled into a shapeless pyre.

As old Mori and Foscari clung to each other, staring at the rearing flames and the smoking rubble, Pugh stood on his own, motionless and indifferent to the heat, staring at the smouldering shafts of the hearse, all that could be seen, all that was left of Tamara's legacy, all that remained of Bocco Detto Banti's paintings.

12

Tamara was in bed when Pugh reached the Casa Calafati. Her face lit up as he appeared but, seeing his expression, she silently rose, put on a dressing gown and started to prepare food for him. By the time it arrived he was sprawled in a chair with a huge whisky, his eyes blank.

'What has happened, caro Piu?' she asked. 'Did things not work out?'

'Yes,' he nodded, his face expressionless, his mind still busy. 'They worked out. We've recovered a haul of drugs and arrested the ringleaders. One got away, but I don't think he'll trouble us again.'

She watched him, worried. 'But something is wrong, Piu?'

His mind was still full of the picture of the burning hearse and he was wondering how to break the news to her.

'Nothing,' he said. 'Nothing's wrong.'

'But you don't smile.'

He wanted to draw some comfort from her sympathy but he didn't wish to worry her, and he knew that it was he himself who should be giving sympathy. He poured himself another whisky and she stared at him, a puzzled expression on her face.

'Tomorrow, you will look like the monster in the play they put on in the puppet theatre,' she said.

'I'll be all right.'

'Perhaps your Captain Jones has discovered I am sharing your room. Your bed also.'

'No, it's not that.'

290

'Then there is nothing to worry about.'

'Yes, there is. A bit.' Suddenly it came out in a rush. 'You've lost your paintings, Tamara. Every last one of them. A bomb hit the place where I had them hidden. The place went up in flames. There's nothing left.'

She lifted her head quickly to look at him, then she studied him gravely. 'I think I would like a cigarette,' she said quietly. She seemed to be fighting an urge to throw her arms round him and was only held back by his expression. 'It doesn't matter, Piu,' she said finally. '*You* are safe and I was worried there would be killing. I had you dead and buried and was saying paters and aves over your coffin. It doesn't matter if you're all right.'

He looked up. 'You've nothing left,' he said. 'Nothing at all. Just that figurine.'

She stared at him, her eyes shining but still touched with worry. 'It is all right, Piu,' she insisted. She made a helpless gesture with her hand and let it drop to her side, struggling to be rational and sensible, to keep her head against his bitterness. 'It will be all right,' she said again. 'You'll see. There was a message from Avvocato Tassinari while you were out. Your professor has arrived. He's come to see the pictures.'

'There's nothing to see.'

'Yes, there is, Piu. You forget. There are three. Small ones. I shall still be richer than I ever thought I was going to be. I never expected anything, so a little – even if it's not the lot – is better than that.'

As he reached out to take her hand, she looked at him with sad, compassionate eyes. 'I think it is late, Piu,' she said softly. 'Perhaps we should go to bed.'

They met at Tassinari's place the following afternoon. Elated by their success over the drugs, Jones was happy to leave everything to Pugh, who borrowed the Jeep and went to the station to pick up his expert.

Though he wore a uniform, he was still a professor, a long, dry, desiccated man who moved slowly but clearly knew what he was talking about. Avvocato Tassinari's man might almost have been his brother, and the two took to each other immediately. They had even heard of each other, had once written to each other before the war, and seemed to regard the meeting as a reunion of old friends.

Tassinari had set up the three small paintings on a table so that they caught the full light from the window. They seemed to glow with colour and restored a little of Pugh's self-confidence, which had been at a low ebb since the night before. Tamara waited quietly alongside him. Their love-making had been urgent and passionate and had left them exhausted, so that she had clung to him, insisting with all the power she possessed that the disaster to the hearse didn't matter.

To his surprise, Marco was also there. He looked sullen but far from poverty-stricken, and again Pugh sensed that the figurine he had caught him trying to sell was not the only thing he had acquired from his brother's possessions.

The two experts studied the paintings for a while in silence, then the Englishman looked at his Italian opposite number and smiled.

'Such splendour,' he said and Tamara looked quickly at Pugh, whose heart thumped suddenly.

'*Che colore!*' The Italian smiled back then they both bent down again, peering at the pictures.

The Italian poked out a lean forefinger, seemed to pluck at the small canvas and nodded, then the Englishman produced a magnifying glass and bent with him. There was an enormous silence and Pugh could feel his breath thick in his throat. Then they rose and turned.

'Absolutely magnificent,' the Englishman said. 'Boccaccio Detto Banti at his very very best. I would date them about 1920. They are English scenes and were painted when he was at his peak. I can identify this one as the *Camp Near Tunbridge Wells*. I've heard of it. I've even seen it. The other two I don't know. But the one on the right with the soldiers seems to be a market in Colchester. It's a street I know well. It was painted at roughly the same time. When Detto Banti was at his best, before he lost his skill, before he returned to Italy and threw in his lot with the Fascists. They are quite remarkable and quite, quite genuine.'

There was a faint snort from Marco. 'They were the only ones that *were* genuine,' he said.

They all turned to him, and he gave a lopsided grin. 'The others were *all* fakes,' he admitted. 'Every one of them, Bocco started them but he never got beyond the outlines. He was hitting the bottle and did nothing more than sketch them out.'

'How do you know this?' Pugh snapped.

'Because *I* painted them. Me. Marcopolo Detto Banti, the man everybody said couldn't paint. I was good enough to fool a lot of people for a long time. It's one of life's ironies, isn't it? Now they're gone I can never boast about it because nobody will ever believe me.'

There was a long silence. The two experts tried to appear absorbed in the small paintings to avoid the embarrassing silence.

'Why?' Tassinari asked.

Marco grinned. 'Because Bocco was no longer able. I'd painted one or two for him which we sold, then the war came and the Germans arrived in Italy. They kept enquiring about his work, and he sold what he had and did well, too. But then he couldn't manage any more so I painted them for him. Sometimes I even had to help him sign them.'

There was a long silence and Marco went on, lacking shame, even a little proud. 'I'd been finishing his paintings for ages,' he said. 'I'd copied his style and I had his paint to work with. I even knew how to mix it because I'd been mixing it for him for a long time. First of all they were just for the Germans. I did them for the gauleiters and senior officers. But then when the

293

experts came and said they were buying for Goering and Hitler himself – for the exhibition hall he wanted to start at Linz – I got scared and stuck them in the cellar. When the Germans were driven out, I decided I'd do better to get the paintings to Naples and sell them to the Americans. Everybody knows the Americans are mad about culture and that there are copies of the Mona Lisa all over the United States. Canalettos, too. I know because when I was over there, I saw more than one that I knew was a fake. I thought, why not Detto Bantis?'

'And the ones from Vicinamontane?'

'Some were what were left over from those I painted for the Germans. Some I painted in the last days before Bocco died. It started when one of the Germans who knew something about art found that he'd already got rid of all his paintings. When he found out I'd helped with them, he said, "Why not paint some more? We can get rid of them." So I did, and we shared the proceeds. The German was eventually posted to Russia. I expect he's dead now.'

'And that's why we never found any preliminary sketches?' Pugh said.

Marco smiled. 'They were mine. I made them. I sold them, too. As genuine Detto Banti sketches, the originals for Detto Banti paintings. I even sold them a Remolo and a Pio Santemara which I said belonged to Bocco.'

'Genuine?'

'Of course not. I knew where to get the right canvas and I mixed the paints by copying from originals. They weren't old masters and I was careful to make mistakes.'

'Mistakes?'

'So I could paint over them. Originals have spontaneity, mistakes that have been painted over. If there's underpainting it indicates authenticity.'

'You studied it well,' Pugh growled.

'It wasn't hard.' Marco smiled. 'I also found two unfinished paintings in Matisse's style and one in

294

Cézanne's. Perhaps Bocco had had ideas himself and lost his nerve.'

'You didn't lose *your* nerve.'

'No. The Germans took them all right. It wasn't difficult. I had his drawings and the remains of his paints and I knew all about his special colours. That red of his and the famous green. And most of the people who came to look at them didn't know anything about art, anyway. When the Germans went I just kept it up.'

Marco shrugged and looked at Tamara. 'You can't grumble,' he said. 'You've got the only genuine ones out of the whole lot.'

Tassinari sighed. 'After all we did to save them,' he murmured.

'Marco gestured. 'You didn't save *them*,' he said. 'They saved *you*.'

There seemed to be plenty of reasons for a celebration. It started at lunchtime and everyone was there – Jones, Tassinari, the two experts, even Paddy O'Mara and Marco Detto Banti. It went on all afternoon and started again in the evening in a private dinner for Pugh and Tamara in a small stone-flagged whitewashed trattoria in a backstreet. The proprietor produced spaghetti and what passed as veal, and instead of the inevitable spinach there were peas which he quietly picked one by one out of the soup. Finally, he recommended for dessert a sort of cake soaked with vermouth, and even went so far, instead of allowing them to find their coffee in a bar, to have it fetched for them, and produced it tepid and almost undrinkable after its long journey to their table.

Pugh and Tamara went home arm-in-arm and made love gently and tenderly. By this time, they had accepted that they belonged to each other and nothing would ever part them, and the warm night convinced them.

Pugh was still elated when he went to the office the next morning. 'It was a good celebration,' he said.

Jones' face didn't slip. 'There's just one thing,' he said in a flat voice.

His manner finally penetrated Pugh's elation. 'What's the matter?' he asked. 'What's the snag?'

'You're the snag. You've been posted.'

'What?' Pleased at their success, delighted suddenly with his life, with discovering he was in love, Pugh felt as if the bottom had dropped out of his world. He had begun to feel settled and domesticated and now the emptiness rushed back. Enormous distances lay before him, and he could feel the wind blowing through them. He forced himself to speak calmly.

'Where to?'

'Tunisia.'

'Who says?'

'Tasker. It was the last thing he did. He was always after you.'

'He's gone now.'

Jones shrugged. 'His report hasn't. It's known you've got a girl in your room and it's against regulations. The powers that be insist.'

Pugh was shocked and indignant. 'For Christ's sake,' he bleated, 'so has Paddy O'Mara! So has Plummer from time to time!'

'They won't have after today if they've got any sense.'

'Probably Tasker had, too.'

'I'm sure he had,' Jones agreed. 'But you're the one who's been named.' He sighed. 'It's ironic, isn't it? You nobble him but just too late to stop him nobbling you. What's called a Pyrrhic victory, I believe.'

'The bloody hypocrite!' The calmness was vanishing and Pugh was growing angry as his quick temper boiled over. 'What the hell does it matter, anyway?'

Jones shrugged. 'Something to do with morals, I think. You know there's been a clamp-down about it. When the police find girls moving in with a soldier, they whizz her off to the *questura*, pile her with others into lorries, take her to the hospital and make her strip to the

296

buff and submit to an examination. The VD rate's been found to be too high.'

'That's a bloody insult!'

'That's exactly what the Italians say. And now that the war looks like ending before too long, our lot are trying to keep 'em sweet because we're going to need 'em. The Italians say it's humiliating because the girls are always given a yellow card, even if they're proved free of disease, and that means they become registered as pros. Some aren't – I know, and everybody knows – and that's what the Italians are complaining about. They want to know why girls are subjected to this humiliation when often it's the soldiers who do the propositioning. The Yanks started clamping down on it long since – big show of propriety – and our lot are now following suit.'

'Tasker's gone now,' Pugh snorted. 'Why can't you just tear up the report?'

'If I had my way I would. But I haven't. Tasker sent the report direct to the general.'

Pugh's fury was passing. 'He never liked me,' he agreed. 'He was just using this as an excuse.'

Jones admitted the fact. 'You're not comfortable to have around,' he said. 'That's the trouble. He was taking a cut from Baracca's operations and you were buggering it up. He was also hoping to get his paws on those Detto Bantis and you buggered that up, too.' He shrugged again. 'I also think pressure's being put on us by everybody – by the gangs, by the authorities who're trying to clean the place up. You were too close. You're dangerous.'

'Can't you speak to the general? After all, we've just put a feather in his bloody cap.'

Jones' own anger finally burst out. 'You don't think, for Christ's sake, that I didn't speak up for you, do you?' he said. 'That I didn't point out what a bloody fine job you've just done? He agreed, and you're going to get a gong and you'll still get your commission – which is a consolation, though in your case, being a bit bloody-minded, you might think it isn't. But you've got to be retired. Shunted to Welfare, put in charge of NAAFI, or the Soldiers', Sailors' and Airmens' Whatsit. Whatever it is, you've got to go. You're out. O-U-T. You can make a name for yourself in Tunisia, but here you're finished.' Jones looked as if he wanted to weep. 'It's one of the seven wonders of the world that a bastard like Tasker can nobble you, old Tom, but he has, he has! By God, he has! And there isn't a thing you can do about it.'

Jones pushed the papers on his desk around for a while, then he looked up, pink in the face. 'The general thought about it a long time but there wasn't much he could do. The complaint had been made and he has to uphold it.'

'A bastard like Tasker!'

'It's not as simple as that. The general doesn't want someone to find you down a back alley with your throat slit. Propaganda comes into it, too, you see. We're just beginning to hold our own with the bloody racketeers, which is why we're making such a fuss about letting everyone know about Tasker and Baracca and Tirandolo, and it would look too bloody bad if our hero – you – got knocked off. The other side would be able to crow that, in spite of minor setbacks, they were still in control.'

Jones looked up with an earnest expression, appealing to Pugh to understand. It made sense, Pugh had to admit, staring through the window at the sea. It was blue with the blue he loved, the blue he'd often tried to paint.

'What about Tamara?' he asked.

Jones frowned. 'Is she important?'

'Yes.'

'I'll keep an eye on her.'

'She might need someone,' Pugh said slowly. 'She's going to be worth a lot of money.'

It was difficult telling Tamara.

'You'll be all right,' Pugh said. 'Avvoccato Tassinari's looking after your affairs and he's as honest as they come. Do what he says. After all, you're not going to be short of money.'

Her eyes were red with weeping. 'What shall I do?'

'Register the pictures.'

'I don't mean the pictures. I mean you. What shall I do without you?'

Pugh didn't know, in the same way that he didn't know what he was going to do without her. He tried to draw her attention away from the problem.

'Place them with a reputable dealer or a gallery. Tassinari will advise you. Then sell them and stick the money in the bank.'

'Must I sell *all* of them. Can't I keep one?'

'That's your affair.' Pugh's face was grim. 'See Captain Jones. He's promised to help, too. Then go somewhere quiet, away from Naples, until it blows over and the armies are gone.'

'You'll be killed.'

'No. The fighting's finished in North Africa.'

'Will you come back?'

'Yes.' The word was bitten off because Pugh knew that, with the war still not over, there were other places he could be sent to.

'I'll wait for you.'

'I've no hold on you.'

She turned on him angrily. 'Of course you have! I've shared your bed. That makes things different.'

'You might meet somebody else. An Italian, like yourself. Somebody younger than me.'

She studied him, a strong figure with curves of humour on his face. It was a face in which she'd seen joy, disappointment and triumph, a face that was capable, as she knew, of tenderness as well as sarcasm. He could be infuriating, unpredictable, but also extravagantly generous, and all the gentleness, all the warm comfort of shared troubles that had sometimes seemed too big for

299

her to bear, came from Pugh in a way she had never had from anyone else.

'I don't think so, Piu,' she said quietly.

Their parting was a long one. He had helped her find a new apartment in the Vomero – which was a much better district, where there was air to breathe – and Tassinari had promised to keep an eye on her.

'It is like having my daughter alive again,' he admitted. 'I'll no longer feel as alone as I did.'

But she had refused to move until Pugh had gone. As they parted, she put her arms round his neck and kissed him fiercely.

'I shall wait,' she said.

'You don't have to. You're a free agent.'

'No,' she insisted. 'I'm not a free agent.' She kissed him again, then she turned abruptly and walked away. In the square nearby she could catch the funicular and, as she paused on the corner, he thought she would turn and wave. But she didn't, and it left him feeling hollow and empty.

When the Jeep came to take him to the harbour, he stood staring at the sea for a while. He wasn't sure what the future held, either for him or for her. He'd said he'd be back and she'd said she'd wait for him. But a lot could happen before he could make it.

The driver shifted restlessly and Pugh realised he was getting impatient.

'I'm coming,' he said.

At the harbour, the ship, a transport converted to carry troops, was waiting. She was tall and high and old-fashioned and smelled of rotten potatoes. She had brought troops from North Africa and was going back virtually empty.

As she swung away from the quayside and moved stern-first to where she could get seaway, the siren boomed and the propeller thrashed the water to a yeasty foam, then the ship's head turned and she began to head southwards.

Staring over the stern as the sea wall grew smaller, linked to the ship now only by the wake and the cries of gulls, Pugh took a deep breath, thinking of all the places he'd sat and slapped on paint. He wondered where Tamara was and what she was doing, and was conscious of a tremendous ache in his chest. Somehow, he decided, he'd come back. He'd make it. He'd come back and find her because in his heart of hearts he knew she would wait for him.

He tossed his cigarette into the sea, then turned and went into the saloon, out of the wind that was bringing with it the last scent of the land before it finally disappeared in the thin, damp smell of the sea.